P.E.
ESSENTIALS

Key Stage 4
GCSE
GNVQ, NVQ, SNVQ

By Doug Neate

First Published 1996

Reprinted, with additions 1996

Reprinted, with amendments 1998

ISBN 0 9520743 2 X

British Library Cataloguing-in-Publication Data.

A catalogue record of this book is available from the British Library.

Printed in Great Britain by the Bath Press, Bath

Contents

**P.E SPORT AND THE
ASSESSMENT OF PHYSICAL ACTIVITIES**

P.E. 2

**FACTORS AFFECTING
PERFORMANCE**

P.E. 3

HEALTH, SAFETY, & TRAINING

P.E.

REASONS, OPPORTUNITIES & ISSUES AFFECTING PARTICIPATION IN PHYSICAL ACTIVITY

ACKNOWLEDGMENTS

I would like to express my thanks to the following people for their help and support in the production of this book.

My wife Mary for her help and advice with many sections of the book, and my children Katie and Joanna, for their patience.

My colleagues and friends at the University of Cambridge Local Examination Syndicate/Midland Examining Board:

Eric Singleton, Director of P.E., Chief Examiner and Principal Moderator GCSE P.E.,

Len Smith, Senior Teacher, Chief Examiner GCSE P.E.

My colleagues and students, past and present, at Charles Keene College, Leicester.

My colleague Mr. David Price, Head of P.E., Countesthorpe College, Leicester.

Mr Peter Faulkner, Head of P.E., Staff and pupils, of the Mountbatten School, Romsey, Hampshire, for their invaluable help in the realisation of, and loan of, photographic material used in the illustration of the book.

Also grateful thanks to Mr David Dunn, Head of P.E., Staff and pupils of St. Peter's School, Southbourne; James Alen's Girls' School, Dulwich; and Dulwich College; for their help in providing photographic opportunities.

Laszlo, Steve, Will, Rebecca, and Jane, for assistance with the artwork.

Gary Simpson, Sue Hunter, Geoff Doré, Eric Singleton, Geoff Messenger, Marie Lord, and Robin Vowles for help with additional photographs.

James Leaver, Helen Farrell and Ann for their help in the preparation of the text, and careful checking of the manuscript.

Sam Denley of Feltham Press for all his hard work and dedication in the design and production of the book.

We would like to thank all the organisations that supplied and granted permission to use their logotypes.

To my wife Mary and children.

Special Notice

Exercise can result in injury, especially those involving weights and apparatus, and must always be supervised by a qualified adult. Neither the author nor the publisher can accept responsible for any injury that may be sustained when performing the exercises described in this book.

Work Packs Available

Photocopiable Teaching Support Packs are available to accompany this book consisting of work sheets designed to help the practising teacher.

PREFACE

The National Curriculum has brought about changes in the School Curriculum, and in the examinations available for pupils and students. New syllabuses develop from, or take account of, the experiences of young people in the Key Stages and the programmes of study.

This text has been designed in accordance with the requirements and terminology of National Curriculum P.E., and the new syllabuses which extend beyond it.

'P.E. ESSENTIALS' provides teachers, and pupils with a broad range of useful and informative material. The themes of the text are all interrelated, it is divided into sections for study purposes only.

AIMS

1 To contribute to the general requirements of Physical Education in the National Curriculum:

   ◆ to promote physical activity and healthy lifestyles;
   ◆ to develop positive attitudes *(fair play, effort, cooperation etc)*;
   ◆ to ensure safe practice.

2 To help develop an understanding and knowledge of the principles involved in safe health–promoting exercise, in line with statements in Key Stage 4 of P.E. in the National Curriculum:

   ◆ to plan, undertake, and evaluate a safe health–promoting exercise programme;
   ◆ to show understanding of the principles involved.

3 To contribute to meeting the assessment objectives of the Qualifications and Curriculum Authority *(QCA)*, regulations for GCSE syllabuses and subject criteria in Physical Education.

Candidates should be able to demonstrate physical performance including their ability to interrelate planning, performing, and evaluating whilst undertaking activity.

Candidates should be able to demonstrate their ability to analyse and improve their own and others' performance.

Candidates should be able to demonstrate their knowledge and understanding of:

   ◆ the factors affecting performance;
   ◆ the health and safety aspects of physical activity, including the advantages and risks associated with a range of training strategies and techniques;
   ◆ the reasons for participating in physical activity.

4 To provide a range of material for teachers, pupils, and students studying foundation and intermediate level P.E., Sport, and Leisure courses including GCSE, BTEC First Diplomas, GNVQ, NVQ, SNVQ, and the Certificate of Further Studies.

5 To provide a foundation for further development and study in this area.

P.E. ESSENTIALS

P.E., Sport & the Assessment of Physical Activities

OBJECTIVES

To enable the reader to understand the following:
◆ Physical Education
◆ P.E. in the National Curriculum at Key Stage 4;
◆ the relationship between P.E. and Games and Sport;
◆ the assessment of physical activities.

1 PHYSICAL EDUCATION (P.E.) AN INTRODUCTION

So what is P.E.? Is it the same as games? Are sports lessons the same as P.E.? What is sport? Confused? Let's try to sort out some of these ideas.

Physical Education involves people in learning and taking part in physical activities. P.E. is often described in physical terms because that's what we can see developing. Teachers, coaches and parents can help you learn physical skills and improve your physical fitness. However, you can't really separate the mind and the body, so P.E. is also about developing the mind through physical activity. It is part of the process of education, through which you can learn to control and coordinate your body.

In P.E. you take part in, and learn about many different physical activities. You try to watch *(observe)*, analyse and improve your own and others' performance in various activities as part of this process. This might give you a real sense of achievement. You will have a better understanding of the activities and of yourself.

Taking part in P.E. could help you develop a more positive attitude towards yourself and towards life. Ideas like competition, cooperation, safety, effort, decision making, and fair play are all important. You might even want to continue participating when you leave school because you enjoy it and get real satisfaction from being involved. Don't be surprised if some people don't enjoy P.E. We're all different, and don't all like the same things.

The teaching of Physical Education occurs in the context of education. It is therefore often described as 'education of and through the physical'.

Physical Education focuses on the movement of the body, involves co-ordination and control, and the development of creativity, enjoyment, and understanding.

The overall aims of P.E. are to develop:

◆ physical skills and abilities;
◆ knowledge and understanding;
◆ positive attitudes to activity and health;
◆ social awareness.

P.E. is an important part of the National Curriculum. You might also be involved in an exam course.

The 1986 and 1988 Education Acts included P.E. as one of the Foundation subjects in the National Curriculum. P.E. is about your involvement in physical activity and a healthy lifestyle. It is also about your attitude to what you do and how you do it, and about being safe at all times.

Six areas of activity are identified in National Curriculum P.E. They are: **Games; Gymnastic Activities; Dance; Athletic Activities** such as running, jumping and throwing**; Outdoor and Adventurous Activities** such as climbing, sailing, skiing, windsurfing, rock-climbing and orienteering**; and Swimming** including floating, going underwater, elementary survival skills, and water safety**.**

At **Key Stage 4**, you should be involved in developing a safe, health-promoting exercise programme, and understand the principles involved. In your examination course these principles should be developed, and a variety of other activities may be assessed *(see The Assessment of Physical Activities: p.9)*.

Action Box

1 From your experiences at school or college, work out how much time you spend on P.E. each week.

2 If you are involved in an exam course in P.E., work out how much time that takes each week.

3 If you are involved in a physical activity outside of school or college, work out how much time that takes each week.

4 Compare the amount of time you spend on these physical activities with the time you spend on other activities like watching TV or playing computer games.

1.1 P.E., Games, Sport, Competition & Fair Play

All pupils study P.E. from ages 5 to 16. The revised National Curriculum P.E. places a greater emphasis on competitive sport and team games, in an effort to raise the importance of these activities in school life. Some of the main points are set out below:

◆ **Key Stage 1** *(5 to 7 years)* – all pupils will learn the skills of competitive games and how to play them.
◆ **Key Stage 2** *(7 to 11 years)* – all pupils will play competitive team games *(including mini versions of the adult games)*.
◆ **Key Stage 3** *(11 to 14 years)* – all pupils will play full individual and team games.
◆ **Key Stage 4** *(14 to 16 years)* – all pupils will play a competitive game along with another activity *(which could be another game)*.

Games

Games are a very popular type of physical activity. Games can be played by individuals, pairs, or teams. The first National Governing Bodies of some team games were formed in this country, and they helped spread the games throughout the world. For example:

◆ The Football Association was founded in 1863;
◆ The first FA Cup competition was held in 1872;
◆ The Football League was established in 1888;
◆ The Rugby Football Union was established in 1871;
◆ The first written and printed rules of Cricket appeared in 1744;
◆ The MCC *(Marylebone Cricket Club)* was formed in 1787, and revised the laws in 1788.

At Key Stage 2 in National Curriculum P.E. Games are divided into three groups.

Net, wall, and target - eg. Volleyball, Squash, Archery, etc.

Invasion - eg. Rugby, Soccer, Hockey, Netball, etc.

Striking/Fielding - eg. Rounders, Softball, Cricket, etc.

What About Sport?

The word sport is used in many different ways. Sport is about a range of specific activities, whereas P.E. is part of the process of education which focuses on the movement of the body. Sport involves competition, and requires physical conditioning *(physical fitness)* or skill or both. Competition is a key part of sport. There have been many attempts to divide sport into groups. Let's examine a few. Brackenridge and Alderson suggested three groups or types.

Game - in this group of sports, you win by out-thinking your opponents, dominating territory, and scoring in some way, *(coincidence, anticipation, avoidance),* eg. Soccer, Hockey, Badminton etc.

Gymnastic - in this group of sports, you win by producing movements which are performed as perfectly as possible when compared to a pre-set standard *(movement replication)*, which are marked by judges, eg. Gymnastics, Trampolining, etc.

Athletic - in this group of sports, you win by producing more power than your opponents *(power optimisation)*, eg. Running, Jumping, Weight Lifting etc.

Specific sports in each of the three types can be analysed by investigating their:

◆ structure *(rules and organisation)*;
◆ strategies *(plans made to win)*;
◆ techniques;
◆ physical demands of the sport *(fitness, energy systems etc.)*;
◆ psychological demands of the sport
   (skill, anxiety control, goal setting etc.).

In 1988 the Sports Council built on the Council of Europe's 'Sport for All' charter of 1976, and divided sport into four broad categories.

Competitive sports - eg. badminton, race swimming, trampolining.

Outdoor pursuits - eg. hill-walking, orienteering and sailing. Individuals challenge, and are challenged by, nature in some way.

Aesthetic movement - eg. figure skating. These activities involve beauty of form, and the idea of self-expression.

Conditioning activities - eg. aerobics, circuit, and weight training. These help individuals maintain or improve their health and fitness.

We could say that, 'Sport is a type of physical activity in which you choose to compete fairly, and try to win'.

School Sport

School sport can provide the basis for a lifelong participation in regular exercise, and the development of mental and moral qualities, including team spirit, sportsmanship, self-discipline, cooperation, commitment, and competing within a framework of agreed rules. School sport can help channel people's energy and aggression in a controlled and constructive way.

The Sportsmark award is available to schools that have effective policies for promoting P.E. and sport, including extra curricular sport *(that is sport outside of the normal P.E. timetable)* which is an important element of school life. The most innovative schools, for example those establishing formal links with local sports club are awarded the Sportsmark Gold for outstanding achievement.

Sports Clubs

Local sports clubs should form links with schools. They could provide a bridge between school sport and centres of excellence; provide school leavers with the opportunity to continue playing sport, and support schools outside of and beyond the National Curriculum. Links could be developed which would enable qualified coaches and local club representatives to visit schools, and pupils to visit local clubs as part of an extra-curricula programme. 'Raising the Game' *(1995)* (see p.131), suggested that clubs could adopt a school. These links will be encouraged by the:

◆ Sports Council's 'Challenge Fund';
◆ Sports Council's requirements for National Governing Bodies to make provision for effective school/club links in their business plans;
◆ Sports Council's regional offices helping schools as much as possible.

For example, in Leicestershire, the Basketball Skills Challenge is a cooperative scheme set up initially between the Leicester Basketball Club *(Leicester Riders)* and Charles Keene College *(a local F.E. College in Leicester),* and then a local travel agency group, and local Primary Schools. By August 1995, the Leicester Riders Basketball Coach had helped develop basketball skills in more than 80 Primary Schools. Sponsorship is now matched by government money through the Sportsmatch scheme.

Club Organisation

For full participation and enjoyment many activities require; special facilities and equipment; specialised coaching and training; and organised events such as matches, and competitions. By joining or getting together to form a club people can share the costs to hire or buy the special facilities and equipment, share in the work to organise teams, coaching and training, arrange events, or put on competitions. Even in solo activities an individual may need to join a club to access facilities, equipment or coaching and meet others to compete against or simply accompany for improved safety *(eg. windsurfing)*.

Clubs bring together people with a common interest socially. Clubs have members, they use facilities, they are involved in competitions and leagues, they are part of local communities, and they advertise in local papers.

At school you might have many types of clubs. Theses could include a gymnastic club, a dance club, and a soccer club. Your local leisure centre might have a swimming club and a martial arts club. There could be an outdoor pursuit centre with a climbing club and a sailing club in your area. You might know of an athletics club at a regional athletics track.

A club normally has a committee which is elected by club members to run the club. Committees have people doing specific jobs:

- a chairperson who controls club meetings;
- a vice-chairperson who can substitute for the chairperson if required;
- a secretary who deals with the paperwork including letter writing and keeping notes *(minutes)* of the meetings;
- a treasurer who deals with financial matters including subscriptions, fees and the payment of bills;
- other members who are elected onto the committee for their expertise, knowledge, or for a specific purpose; e.g. a social secretary; a health and safety officer; a coaching secretary; a representative for the members. Some clubs also have a fund raising officer.

Clubs normally belong to governing bodies and provide insurance for their members through their governing body affiliation *(membership)*.

Competitions

There are many different ways of organising competitions, let's examine a few.

- Knockout competitions are easy to organise and are used when competition entry is large. 'Rounds' are held from which only the winner advances. In each round the numbers remaining are halved until the final is reached, e.g. 64 → 32 → 16 → 8 → 4 → 2. Competitors knocked out early only play one match. If the number of competitors does not exactly meet the number required in a round, 'byes' *(no match played)* are given *(usually drawn for)*.
- Round Robin competitions take time and are often used when the competition entry is small, so that competitors play more than one match. All competitors play each other and the results recorded. The winner is the one with the best record.
- Ladders involve a list of individuals in order of ability *(of performance)*. It's possible to challenge competitors above you on the ladder *(a rule is usually set limiting the number of places above that you can challenge e.g. 4)* and if you win you move up the ladder.
- Leagues involve competitors playing each other at least once *(often twice)* and points are awarded for a win, a loss, or a draw. At the end of the season a league champion emerges *(individual or team with the most points)*. The league champion may be promoted to a higher league and the bottom competitors relegated *(demoted)* to a lower league. As leagues become bigger they tend to divide into first, second and third leagues etc.

Table Tennis Mixed Doubles Knockout			
First Round	**Quarter Finals**	**Semi Finals**	**Final**
Sue & Fred			
Bill & Debs	Bill & Debs		
Jane & Pip	Jane & Pip		
Clare & Joe		Jane & Pip	
Ann & John		Josy & Olly	
Suzy & Pete	Suzy & Pete		
Sally & Geff	Josy & Olly		
Josy & Olly			Josy & Olly
Sara & Cliff			Chas & Carly
Chas & Carly	Chas & Carly		
Jenny & Tim	Jenny & Tim		
Gwen & Rik		Chas & Carly	
Anna & Bob		Bev & Steve	
Bev & Steve	Bev & Steve		
Shel & Colin	June & Mick		
June & Mick			

Question Box　?

From what you have read, try to answer these questions.

1 What are the six areas of activity in National Curriculum P.E.?

2 What do you think P.E. is now?

3 Do you think P.E. and sport are the same?

4 On what does the revised National Curriculum P.E. place more emphasis?

Rules and fair play are essential, they are at the very heart of sport and physical activities, ensuring everyone enjoys full participating in safety.

Fair Play

Have you noticed how people feel when a team or individual they support wins a competition. But what if they are caught cheating? Competitors are expected to try to win, but only within the rules. Winning should not be at all costs.

Sport is based on these two ideals of trying hard to win or performing to the best of your ability, whilst respecting the rules, and playing fairly. Fair play and effort are at the heart of sport. The Olympic Oath, which is repeated by a representative from each team during the opening ceremony, illustrates these ideals.

"We swear that we will take part in these Olympic Games in the true spirit of sportsmanship, and that we will respect and abide by the rules that govern them, for the glory of sport and the honour of our country"

The ancient Olympic Games went into decline when fair competition was replaced by a 'win at all costs' attitude *(see Participation, Excellence, and the Olympic Ideal: p.138).*

1.2 The Assessment of Physical Activities

During Key Stage 4, and in many exam courses you might be involved with, you could be assessed in your chosen physical activities. National Curriculum P.E. identifies six areas of physical activity.

- Games
- Gymnastic Activities
- Dance
- Athletic Activities
- Outdoor and Adventurous Activities
- Swimming

Games are divided into;

- net, wall, and target,
- invasion,
- striking and fielding.

Your performance, and the performance of others, are the focus for the assessment process. It is in relation to performance that your ability to plan, evaluate, analyse and improve will be judged.

Planning, Performing, & Evaluating

Participation in physical activities involves you in the processes of planning, performing, and evaluating. Part of this process involves the development of a safe health-promoting exercise programme which is related to the activities in which you are involved.

You might need to write down the details of the programme in relation to your chosen activity. You would need to assess your skill, fitness, and/or performance levels before you start.

Let's examine some of the possible elements involved in the assessing of planning, performing, and evaluating.

Planning

- How well have you learned the rules and regulations of the activity?
- How well have you physically prepared yourself?
- Have you considered safety issues?
- Have you organised your equipment?
- Have you learned the skills of the activity?
- How well do you understand and apply tactics and strategies before and during the activity?
- How well have you mentally prepared yourself?

Performing

- How well do you make the ' right' decisions when you need to?
- How well can you consistently perform the skills in various situations ?
- How well does your body cope with the physical demands of the activity?
- Do you control your anxiety levels?
- How effective is your performance?

Careful observation is needed for proper assessment of physical performance.

I With the help of your teacher develop a plan for a safe health-promoting exercise programme which is related to the activity (*activities*) you participate in.

● Make sure you have a title.

● Identify the warm-up exercises involved and how long you would spend doing them.

● Identify any skills you would need to learn/improve and organise a programme to develop them.

● Make sure you actually perform the activity.

● Identify the fitness components involved and organise a programme to develop them.

● Identify the warm-down (*cool-down*) exercises involved and how long you would spend doing them.

You should be practical and realistic; set your goals in small steps; use the principles of training and of movement; ideas of skill, learning, motivation, mental preparation, fitness, safety, balanced diet (*see Balanced Diet p.83*), etc. Identify how long you would spend at each stage, and lay out a calendar to complete the programme.

2 Show your ideas to your teacher and discuss them. Remember to evaluate your programme and look for ways of improving it.

Video recording allows careful analysis of fast actions.

How effective your performance is might involve the quality of your performance; and/or it's creativity, as for example in gymnastics and dance. In other activities it might involve the outcome of your performance; for example in different types of games, athletics, swimming, and outdoor and adventurous activities.

You also need to consider the idea of aesthetic appreciation (*beauty, gracefulness, interpretation*). This is important in activities such as gymnastics and dance where the body is used to reproduce a movement perfectly or to communicate an idea or a theme to an audience. We often refer to form and style. Form involves a level of performance (*performance form as in games*) or the manner in which a movement is made (*stylised form as in gymnastics*). Style is an individual or team quality which can be seen in the way a movement is performed or the way a team plays.

Evaluating

◆ How well do you make moment by moment checks of the situation you are in, and do you act accordingly?

◆ How well do you consider your performance after you have finished, and evaluate your feelings?

Planning, performing, and evaluating, form a continuous and interrelated process. You could use a video recording to observe yourself and others. If others are on the tape remember to wear clearly identifiable coloured bibs etc. Ask your teacher if this is possible, and start to look at yourself in relation to the ideas of planning, performing, and evaluating.

Analysing & Improving

Analysing and Improving performance focuses on your ability to:

◆ analyse your own and others' performance;

◆ identify ways that your own and others' performance can be improved.

You would need to participate in and observe performance in order to do this. You would need to understand the movements, tactics, strategies, rules, and roles of participants. Video can be used as part of this process. You could referee, choreograph, and officiate, as well as perform.

Let's examine some of the possible elements involved in the assessment of analysing and improving performance.

Analysing

◆ How well can you analyse your own performance?
◆ How well can you analyse the performance of others?
◆ How well can you referee, umpire, coach, or choreograph, etc?
◆ How well can you analyse the skills involved?
◆ How well can you analyse various training methods?

Improving

◆ How well can you consider the effect different training methods might have on the improvement of performance?
◆ How well do you set goals and record your progress in reaching them *(skill, fitness etc.)*?
◆ How well can you identify what you *(or others)* would need to do to improve, and put these ideas into practice?

So where do you begin? You need to know the rules, regulations, skills, strategies, and the physical and psychological demands of your activities. You need to understand and consider the following.

◆ Factors affecting performance *(see section Two)*.
◆ Health, safety, and training *(see section Three)*.
◆ Reasons, Opportunities, and Issues affecting participation *(see section Four)*;

All of these must be related to the physical activities you take part in, and the development of a safe, health-promoting exercise programme. Your teachers will guide and advise you, and they will assess you regularly. A moderator *(someone who checks that you are being assessed correctly)* might also watch you, and look at your work. Arrangements must be made so that pupils with disabilities are not disadvantaged.

At Key Stage 4, pupils:

"demonstrate increasingly refined techniques in their selected activities. Their performance is more consistent and effective. They anticipate responses from others and use this information to adapt their own performance. They undertake different roles, such as performer, coach, choreographer and official. They evaluate accurately and make judgements using relevant technical terms. They regularly participate in health-promoting physical activity, and show an understanding of the principles used to prepare and monitor an exercise programme for a healthy lifestyle."

Exceptional Performance refers to when:

"pupils demonstrate outstanding ability in at least two activities, showing a high degree of consistency and effectiveness in their performance. They understand and apply increasingly advanced techniques. They show initiative and independence in organising activities for themselves and others. They devise and use appropriate criteria for judging and improving their own and others' performance using relevant technical terms accurately and confidently. They plan, undertake and evaluate an appropriate health-promoting exercise programme, showing a thorough understanding of the principles involved and with due regard to safety".

(Department for Education (now DFEE), 1995, P.E. in the National Curriculum.)

Action Box

1 With the help of your teacher develop a programme to observe, analyse, and improve skill(s).

2 Choose any one skill, and ask a class mate to perform it for you under safe supervised conditions.

3 Observe and analyse what they do

4 To analyse their performance make two lists, the first should highlight what they did well, and the second should highlight what could be improved.

5 Now work out ways in which they could improve their performance. Write your ideas down, and with your teacher's permission discuss them in class.

KEYWORDS

- P.E.
- National Curriculum
- Sports Council
- Sport
- Olympic Oath
- Competition
- School Sport
- Sports Clubs
- Club Organisation
- Competitions
- Fair Play
- Rules
- Assessment
- Physical Activities
- Participation
- Planning
- Performing
- Evaluating
- Analysing
- Improving
- Safe
- Health-promoting exercise
- Moderator

CHECK LIST

✔ P.E. involves people in learning & performing physical activities.

✔ P.E. should be enjoyable & satisfying.

✔ P.E. is part of the process of education.

✔ P.E. is part of the National Curriculum.

✔ There are six areas of activity in National Curriculum P.E.

✔ Competitive Sport is about competing fairly.

✔ The revised P.E. National Curriculum places more emphasis on competitive sport & team games.

✔ Schools & clubs should develop links.

✔ The Assessment of Physical Activities involves planning, performing, evaluating, analysing, & improving.

✔ The Assessment of Physical Activities involves the development of a safe, health-promoting exercise programme which is related to the activities in which you are involved.

P.E. ESSENTIALS

Factors Affecting Performance

OBJECTIVES

To enable the reader to understand the following factors that affect performance.

- Skill
- Learning, motivation, and mental preparation.
- Physical Fitness
- Physique *(physical build)*
- Personality and Performance
- Age and Gender
- Equipment and Surfaces

Action Box

2 SKILL

When you improve your skills you perform better. You feel good when you learn new skills, and this can help motivate you. The quality of your performance is largely determined by your skill.

Although most people feel that there is no particular problem in understanding what skill means, it is difficult to get everybody to agree to a definition.

There are many different types of skills, for example social skills, mental skills *(see Mental Practice: p.29)*, and physical skills. All are involved in P.E., but the emphasis is on physical skills.

Physical skills involve the movement of your body. The nervous system, which is made up of the brain, spinal cord, nerves, and sense organs; organise, control, and coordinate the muscles to move or position your body with precision *(see The Nervous System: p.76)*.

Different skills are needed to perform and participate in different activities. With practice you become familiar with the skills, master them, do them without thinking, and you become skilful. These movement skills are normally called Motor Skills.

2.1 Motor Skills

The word motor emphasises the most obvious part of the skill, the physical movement itself. *(Unless otherwise stated all skills referred to throughout the book are motor skills.)* Motor skills take time to learn. They are the result of a complicated series of mental and physical processes, developed through practise, and happen very quickly when the skill is performed.

Gross Motor Skills

Some motor skills involve the movement of large groups of muscles. These are called Gross Motor Skills. Javelin throwers, and dancers when they jump, use large blocks of muscles to produce powerful skilful movements.

Fine Motor Skills

Other motor skills involve the movement of small groups of muscles, these are called Fine Motor Skills. The delicate action to produce the spin of a table tennis ball, and the final wrist movements in a badminton shot are examples of Fine Motor Skills.

Gross and Fine Motor Skills often work together in a motor skill to produce both powerful movements and fine control in a coordinated way.

For successful performance fine and Gross Motor skills need to be performed consistently.

To quickly get into the best position this player has used gross motor skills, to accurately hit and direct the shuttlecock she will use fine motor skills.

Skill as a Learned Ability

The development of skills involves learning movements, which are not always obvious or easy. These movements are learnt during a number of organised practice sessions. The success or failure of this learning is judged by assessing the improvement in performance.

The reason for developing skills is to improve performance. This involves better control of your actions, making fewer mistakes, and using your available energy better. When you have learned a skill, you don't feel as tired performing it as you did when you were learning it.

Let's look at two swimmers. One photo shows a good swimmer who is moving through the water in a smooth, coordinated way. Actions are being controlled correctly, and energy used efficiently. The other shows someone who is less skilled. There is less control of the actions, energy is being wasted, and mistakes are being made. We can see this from the extra splashing.

Good coaching and teaching tries to make sure that skills are learned in the right way. Bad habits are difficult to break.

We could say that skill is the learned ability to perform in a physical activity, efficiently *(you do not waste time or energy)*, successfully *(you improve and perform to the best of your ability)*, and consistently *(you can rely on performing well on most days)*.

Question Box ?

1 Can you tell which one of the swimmers shown in the two photographs is more skillful?

2 If you can, how do you know?

Different people have different abilities, which suit them for different activities, so regardless of the amount of time spent practising a learnt skill, they will reach different levels. Most top class performers do similar training, and are equally motivated, but differences still persist. Success is about improving, and doing your very best at all times.

What About Technique?

In everyday speech about performance, the words skill and technique are often thought to mean the same thing as it is difficult to differentiate between the two.

Techniques are the basic patterns of movement which have to be developed in every activity.

You can practise techniques by themselves, but need to learn to use techniques in the right way. Skilful performance could be said to be the suitable use of the correct technique.

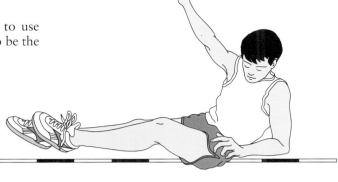

Two high jumpers skilfully using two different techniques.

'Fosbury Flop'

'Scissors'

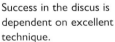

Success in the discus is dependent on excellent technique.

2.2 Dividing Skills into Groups

There are many different ways of dividing skills into groups. Let's examine one way of doing it.

Skills can be divided into open and closed types. The division between open and closed skills is based on the type of situation, or environment, in which the skills are used.

Open Skills

Open skills are performed in situations which continually change. You have to keep adapting to the changes as they happen. Skills like intercepting passes, and moving into position to receive passes are performed in these changing conditions. You need to adapt to meet whatever may happen. Successful performance depends on your ability to see what's going on, accurately interpret what's happening, anticipate, and act in the right way at the right moment.

Closed Skills

Closed skills are performed in predictable and stable conditions. You have to try and produce the movement in the same way each time. Skills like cartwheels *(artistic gymnastics)*, seat drops *(trampolining)*, formation dance, and free shots *(basketball)* are like this. The development of the 'feeling' of the movement is important in controlling your performance. Receptors *(receivers)* in muscles, tendons and joints, called proprioceptors, send this 'feeling' type of information via sensory nerves to the brain.

Skills Continuum

The two types of skill are not always totally separate, they can be considered as being at either end of a continuous system or continuum. Between the two ends of the continuum are skills made up of both open and closed elements. A continuum is a line which allows for skills made up of open and closed elements to be shown.

The volley in squash has a strong movement pattern which has to be adapted to the situation in which you find yourself. This type of skill would lie somewhere in the middle of the continuum.

Open skills in a game of rugby.

Dancing a well rehearsed routine involves closed skills.

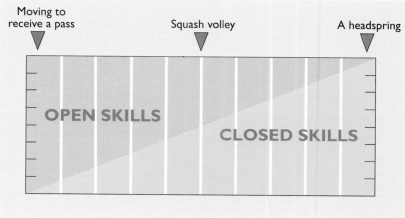

2.3 Skills Practice

All skills should be practised under conditions as close as possible to those that they are going to be performed in. Open skills need to be practised in situations which involve change. The amount of change may be restricted by the teacher, so that a particular situation can be isolated and practised. The performer needs to practise the skill in a flexible way, learning to adapt.

Closed skills need to be practised in exactly the same way each time. Repetitive practice, emphasising the same elements over and over again is required. In a performance, the skill would have to be performed in the same way each time.

Skills with open and closed elements need both types of practice.

When any of these skills are performed, other factors also affect us, and cause our performance to vary. These factors include the level of motivation, and anxiety *(worry)* (see p.47).

Action Box

From the following list identify;

1 which skills are open;

2 which skills are closed;

3 which skills are in between:

   a) backward roll on the floor;

   b) badminton drop shot;

   c) tennis volley;

   d) intercepting a pass in hockey;

   e) trampoline somersault.

Skills like the tennis serve and hurdling are practised repetitively in order to perfect the action, but both would be subject to some change when performed under different conditions eg. surface & weather..

2.4 Thinking & Doing/Information Processing

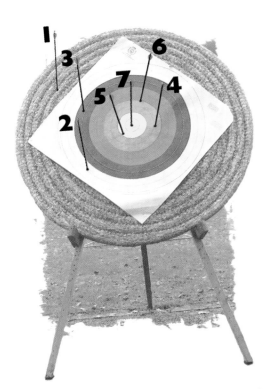

The movements you make can be seen and tested. The thinking that goes on before you move is difficult to examine because the results of your thinking can't be seen until you move. One way of trying to explain this process is to build a model.

When you are learning a skill you receive information *(input)*, think about the information, decide what to do *(decision making)*, perform an action *(output)*, and have information fed back to you about the movement itself and what happened *(feedback)*. Let's block these ideas into a simple diagram.

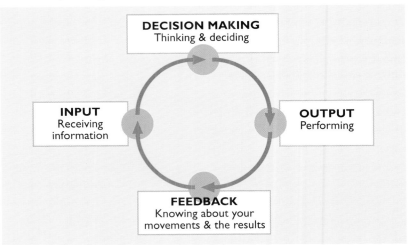

This model is called information processing. It tries to explain what goes on when you turn information you receive into movements.

Let's look at the four main parts of this model in more detail.

Input

The information you receive is called input. You receive information from your senses - sight, sound, touch, taste, smell, and the 'feel' of your muscles and skeletal system.

Decision Making

The input is analysed and processed by the brain and given meaning by comparing it with your memory. This involves both conscious and subconscious *(automatic)* elements. Decisions are then made to produce the right actions at a particular instant. Any performance involves continual decision making.

In the early stages of performing a skill, you have to concentrate on what you are doing. As the skill is learned, decisions about movements become automatic, and you have more time to make conscious decisions about tactics and strategies, style and expression, and fine tuning *(see Stages of Learning: p.27)*.

Perception and memory are both necessary elements in decision making. Error develops if these are inaccurate. The interaction between accurate perception and memory ensures that correct decisions are made.

Feedback helps you make decisions during your performance. It is not easy to see this happening, but in some sports such as bowls and archery you can follow how feedback has influenced a succession of actions.

Study the photograph above. The arrows are numbered in the order that they were shot. Can you work out how the archer adjusted their aim after s/he shot each arrow?

Perception

In order to make a decision you must give meaning to what you have seen, heard, and felt. This is called perception and is a first step in interpreting information. Perception acts as a filter and helps you separate out the important information from the unimportant. Different people have different interpretations of the same information or event. This often happens and may lead to disagreement between performers and officials.

Memory

To make a correct decision you have to compare your interpretations of events with your memories and experiences. Memory is basically a storage and retrieval *(finding)* system. You need to be able to remember what you've learned so that you can use it when you need to. Memory is often described as being in two parts, short term memory, and long term memory.

Short term memory - This has a limited capacity, and information can only be stored here for a relatively short time. It is in short term memory for example that the learned parts of a new skill are organised, before being passed onto and stored in long term memory.

Long term memory - Long term memory has an almost infinite capacity, and information stored here lasts for a long time, often for a lifetime. To get information from short term memory to long term memory you have to use it enough, and code the information in some way. Coding gives information a memory key which enables you to retrieve it when you want to. In P.E. these memory keys are usually physical in nature. When you learn to ride a bike the key involves the balance required. Years later this balance point can quickly be regained by getting on a bike. The memories are unlocked and, although you may be out of practise if you haven't ridden for many years, the skill returns if it was properly learned in the first place, and the information stored in long term memory.

How much can you handle?

Limited Channel Capacity - A large amount of information is affecting you during complex physical activities like Badminton. You can become confused because you can only deal with a limited amount of information at once. This is called limited channel capacity.

Overloading & Selective Attention - With limited channel capacity you could become overloaded with information, and be unable to cope with what's going on. You might not know what information to select and to concentrate on. You might need a teacher to help you learn to focus your mind *(attention)* on the important information *(selective attention)*.

Whose advantage?

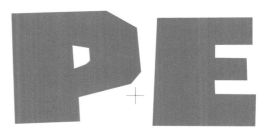

Stare at the cross for 30 seconds, then stare at a plain white surface.

Which line is the longest?

What do you see?

It's school sports day, is the runner catching up twice as tall as the race leader or less?

1 The importance of feedback in a skill can be shown in many activities, eg; Basketball.

2 A group *(20+ is best)* divides up into pairs and twenty shots are taken from the free throw line by everyone and the scores noted.

3 While awaiting their turn the main group should try to keep away from the basket(s), so that each pair, one shooting as one observes, are not distracted.

4 When finished, the scores are added up for the whole group.

5 The whole procedure is then repeated, except, after aiming, the shooter MUST LOOK AWAY as they throw, so that they do not see what happens to the ball, the observer notes the score but must not help the shooter.

6 You could also cover their ears with headphones to block out the sound that the ball makes when it hits the basket/backboard/wall etc. Be careful!

7 Then add up the group scores.

8 You should find that without the knowledge of results the group scores get worse.

Question Box ?

From what you have read, try to answer these questions.

1 What is a motor skill?

2 What is an open skill?

3 What is a closed skill?

4 What is memory?

5 How can feedback help in improving performance?

Motor Programmes

Skills are stored as motor programmes. These are patterns of muscle commands which can be used quickly when needed.

Output

Movement is called output. Movements are made by muscles controlled by the brain via motor nerves. Movements become more energy efficient, and coordination improves as you become more skillful.

Feedback

When you've made your decision, and performed the skill, you need to receive information about what has happened, so that you know what to do next time you try the same skill. Without this feedback you would not know whether your actions were correct, or whether the result was right or wrong. Feedback helps you improve your performance, and the sooner you receive it the better. It is difficult to learn or correct your actions without feedback. Feedback involves two types of knowledge.

Knowledge of Results (KR) - This is about the result of your actions. This is called knowledge of results *(KR)*, and focuses on what the outcome is, eg. the tennis serve landed out.

Knowledge of Performance (KP) - This supplies you with information about the nature of your performance. When you served your arm might have been bent when it should have been straight, or your head might have rotated forward instead of staying upright.

You can get this feedback in different ways.

Intrinsic Feedback - You could feel that your arm was bent, and see or hear the result of your actions *(KP/KR)*. Information you receive from yourself like this is called intrinsic feedback.

Extrinsic Feedback - Alternatively a coach could tell you that your arm was bent, and/or that you had scored *(KP/KR)*. This coach based information is extra to your own, and is called extrinsic feedback or supplementary feedback.

Importance of Feedback

All of this information is useful and important. Always make sure that you understand the information that you have received before you try again. Let's identify some useful principles about feedback.

◆ You cannot learn without feedback. Without information about the performance or the result, improvement is difficult if not impossible.
◆ It should be available as soon as possible. It should not be delayed.
◆ Feedback should be accurate, specific and as brief as possible.
◆ Learners must have enough time to think about the information they have received before they try again.
◆ Teachers should always check that feedback has been understood.
◆ Feedback is important in planning, performing, evaluating, analysing, and improving performance.

You can always test the affect any particular type of feedback has on performance by removing that type of feedback and seeing what happens to the performance.

2.5 Reaction, Movement & Response Time

The relationship between the reaction time, movement time, and response time can be shown in a simple equation.

Reaction time + Movement time = Response time

It is easy to confuse these three terms, and in everyday language people talk about having fast reactions rather than fast responses, but as you will see they have quite different meanings.

Reaction Time

When you try to respond to the unanticipated actions of other people there is a delay before you act. This delay period is called reaction time. It is the time it takes your brain to receive the information, to decide what to do, and to send impulses to the muscles.

Movement Time

The time it takes to actually move is called the movement time. Once the movement has begun it has to be controlled. Some believe that the movement is controlled by automatic pre–programmed motor programmes which are learned and used when needed, others believe that feedback is used to make adjustments as you act. Perhaps both happen, depending on the speed of your movement. In really fast movements there may not be enough time to use feedback information *(see Feedback p.22)* to modify the action.

Response Time

Response time can be measured with an electronic response timer, by timing the delay between the appearance of a signal such as a light and someone pushing a button.

A simpler method is the 'dropped ruler test' in which the distance the ruler drops before a person can trap it between their fingers is taken as a measure of their response time.

Your reaction time is fixed by the nature of your nervous system, but training and practise can improve your movement time, and experience can result in you anticipating situations better.

Response *(reaction)* timer.

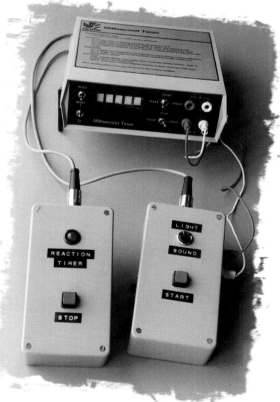

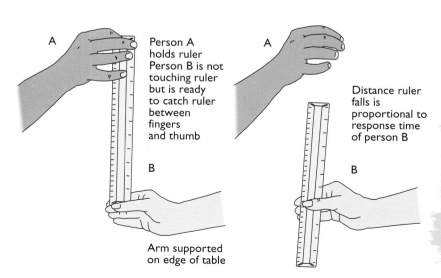

Person A holds ruler Person B is not touching ruler but is ready to catch ruler between fingers and thumb

Arm supported on edge of table

Distance ruler falls is proportional to response time of person B

2.6 What About Forgetting

How is it that we forget so much? Why things are forgotten is not fully understood. Perhaps it is because the information was never properly learned or coded in the first place. There are several ideas which try to explain how information might be forgotten.

Trace decay

This means the fading or decaying of the memory in the brain once something has been learned but not practised or used. If something isn't used for a long time the memory of it simply slowly fades away.

Interference

The idea of interference suggests that forgetting may be caused by different pieces of information interfering with one other. For instance, existing information can interfere with new learning, eg. a tennis player might find the previously learned skills of tennis interfering with the learning of badminton skills. Also interference from outside sources can occur during the period between two practice sessions *(see also p.29)*.

Coding

It might be that the problem is in remembering the coding, rather than the information itself. If information is coded and stored, then the code has to be remembered. If this is forgotten the memory remains locked away.

Memory training

Concentrate on training your memory just as you train your muscles. Try to practise regularly, and make sure you are practising the right way. Don't try to learn new things when you are very tired. Always concentrate on what you are doing.

KEY WORDS

- Skill
- Central Nervous System
- Motor Skill
- Gross Motor Skill
- Fine Motor Skill
- Technique
- Open Skills
- Closed Skills
- Information Processing
- Perception
- Memory
- Decision Making
- Limited Channel Capacity
- Overloading
- Selective Attention
- Controlling Movement
- Feedback
- Knowledge of Results
- Knowledge of Performance
- Extrinsic Feedback
- Intrinsic Feedback
- Response Time
- Reaction Time
- Movement Time
- Forgetting

CHECK LIST

✔ Movement/physical skills are called motor skills.

✔ Motor skills are organised & controlled by the Central Nervous System.

✔ Motor skills which involve large muscle groups are called Gross Motor Skills.

✔ Motor skills which involve small muscle groups are called Fine Motor Skills.

✔ Skill is learned & makes performance more consistent, efficient and effective (successful).

✔ Skill can be divided into open & closed types.

✔ Information processing is a model of how we learn and perform skills.

✔ Perception and memory are important elements in making a decision.

✔ Feedback is information you receive about your actions.

✔ $\text{Response time} = \text{reaction time} + \text{movement time}$

3 LEARNING, MOTIVATION & MENTAL PREPARATION

You need to be motivated to concentrate and learn properly. Learning enables you to improve your performance and be more successful.

Success = learning skills + physical conditioning + mental preparation

You need to develop your skills, physical fitness *(conditioning)*, and mental preparation.

3.1 Learning

In all physical activities, learning is assessed by measuring performance. This assumes that performance is a good measure of learning. It may not be! Performance levels go up and down constantly, depending on how we feel, the weather and interactions with other people. Performances are snapshots of how much we have learned, combined with all those other factors that are affecting us at the time of the performance. A one-off snapshot is not always accurate. Learning is supposed to bring about a sense of stability, and of permanence, to performance. Bringing consistency to performance is one problem with which the National Coaching Foundation and the Governing Bodies of Sport, are concerned *(see NCF: p.133, and National Governing Bodies of Sport: p.124).*

Learning Curves

To find out how much someone has really learned, you would need to test them regularly, and plot the results to produce a learning curve. Each performance adds another 'snapshot' to the curve. Over a period of time it is possible to see how a performer is progressing.

There isn't a single curve of learning. Each person produces their own curve. However, some typical shapes have appeared in many curves, and these shapes can tell us how the individual is doing. To plot a curve requires a comparison between the number of practice trials and the performance scores. Let's examine a few typical shapes.

Linear Curve - This shape shows that the rate of improvement of performance is directly proportional to the number of practice sessions, that is as the number of practice sessions increase so does the rate of improvement of performance.

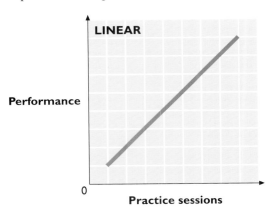

Curve of Negative Acceleration *(or decreasing gains)* - This shape shows that the individual has performed better in earlier sessions than in later ones, and that the rate of performance improvement is slowing.

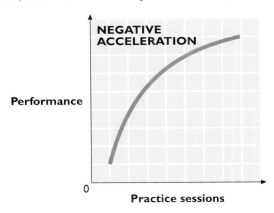

Curve of Positive Acceleration *(or increasing gains)* - This shape shows that the individual has performed better in the later sessions than in the earlier ones, and that the rate of performance improvement is getting faster.

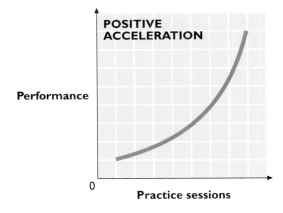

Plateau Curve - This shape appears flat and is often referred to as a period in which nothing seems to be happening. This often occurs when the individual is trying to do too much at once. In fact the individual may be learning, but this will only show itself at the end of the flat part of the curve or plateau. A major problem when a plateau occurs, is not only that performance does not improve, but that individuals feel that they are getting nowhere; they can become bored, tired, and feel like giving up. It is best to organise practice sessions to avoid plateaus occurring. If they do happen, the teacher must keep morale up and interest going. Performers have to believe that they will succeed. It might be necessary to reset the goals that have been agreed, and introduce more short term targets in order to build steadily and overcome the plateau.

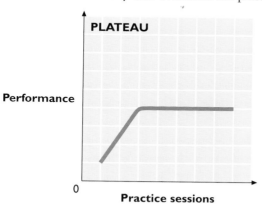

Associative stage of learning requires assistance.

Training can be adapted to make the most of an individual's learning curve. Goals can be adjusted if necessary, and problems discussed. The results themselves can be used to motivate performers, and build self-confidence. This helps performers to cope when they become anxious.

Stages of Learning

Learning occurs in three stages, the cognitive stage, the associative stage, and the autonomous stage.

Cognitive Stage - Beginners must first understand what they have to do, this is called the cognitive stage. Once they understand what has to be done, they can begin to practise.

Associative Stage - When they start to practise they concentrate on the movement they are trying to learn, and motor programmes begin to be laid down, this is called the associative stage. In the early stages of learning, beginners can make dramatic improvements in their performance. As they get better, the rate of improvement slows down. They must be reassured that this is a normal part of the process.

Autonomous Stage - This is the stage when the skill being learned becomes more and more automatic. As performers improve they appear to have more time and more balance and poise, they begin to have time to think about tactics, strategies, style, expression, and the fine tuning of skills.

Individuals may get stuck at any stage of learning, and may need help to overcome the block and make progress. Recording progress is one way of monitoring performance and identifying when help is required.

Autonomous stage achieved.

Different types of practice can be investigated in the following way.

1 A skill is chosen to practise.

2 Eight people are tested on their performance of the skill. They are then divided into two equal groups of four *(based on their performance of the skill)*.

3 One group practises these skills for up to 30 minutes without a break.

4 The other group practises for five minutes, and has a two minute break. This is repeated six times. Care is taken.

5 Each group is tested after the practice session.

6 The results are compared.

7 Each person is asked what they felt about their practice session.

8 With your teacher's permission discuss your findings in class.

Practice may not always make perfect but it always helps.

What's the Best Way to Learn a Skill?

You can try to learn a skill either by breaking it down into its basic parts, or by trying to learn it as a whole.

Parts learning

This is when a skill is broken down into distinct parts or stages, each part is learnt separately, and then all the parts are put together into the complete skill.

Progressive parts - This is when someone learns each stage in sequence from start to finish, joining them together as they go along, until the complete skill is learnt.

Whole learning

This is when a skill is learnt all at once, as a whole.

Whole-Part-Whole - When the skill has been learnt as a whole, it is possible to identify any element that is faulty, and to improve it independently from the whole skill. The success of this process is judged when the whole skill is tried again, this is called whole-part-whole learning.

All these approaches can work. If you believe that you can cope with the basic needs of a skill, even if you would have to work hard, the whole method could be used. If you feel that the skill is too difficult for you to learn as a whole, the parts method could be used. If you choose to use the parts method, make sure you know what the whole skill consists of before you start.

The whole method allows the pace and flow of the skill to be maintained. The parts method reduces the complexity of a skill. Whichever method is used, make sure that all the safety precautions have been followed.

Having decided on the best method it then remains for you to decide how the practice sessions are going to be organised.

How can practice be organised?

Learning a skill can take a lot of practise. None of us have limitless time available, therefore practise needs to make the most efficient use of the time that we have. Teachers and coaches can help us to learn skills in the shortest possible time. Practice sessions therefore have to be organised to enable this to happen.

Massed practice

One way is to practise continually without rests. This is called massed practice. The the skill is continually practised and the learner has no rest periods. The learner has to be constantly involved in the practice. In true massed practice there are no breaks in performance.

Distributed practice

Another way is to break the session up into relatively smaller units with rest periods between them. This is called distributed practice. If you test people straight after the session, distributed practice produces better results. This is because the learners are not as tired after distributed practice. They have had rests as part of the session.

Research has shown that in the long term, learning and performance results are relatively equal using either method. It is a sensible idea to relate the length of the practice session to your ability, and to the difficulty of the activity. Only do what you can cope with in a way that makes sense to you.

Skill practice is all about quality. When learning new skills, once you become tired or bored, you need to rest. Always try to practise the skill in the same manner and situation as you are going to perform it.

Mental Practice

Mental practice is also very important. You should practise regularly by imagining *(visualising)* the movements in your head, and seeing yourself succeeding. You can practise strategies and tactics, and improve your confidence, attitude, control of aggression, control of anxiety, and concentration using mental practice. The image in your head should be real and detailed. Mental practice, when used with physical practice, can help you learn physical skills. Mental practice should be a regular part of your training programme and event preparation. Don't forget that the mind controls the body.

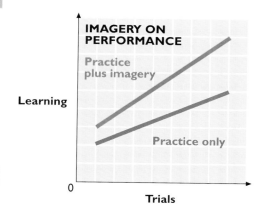

Transfer of Training *(learning)*

Some skills already learned for one physical activity can 'transfer' to a new skill, and/or physical activity. The value of this transfer of training *(learning)* appears to depend on the amount of similarity between the skills and the activities.

◆ Helpful *(positive)* transfer is most likely when the action involved in the new skill or activity is similar to the action involved in the old skill or activity *(tennis serve - volleyball overarm serve)*

◆ Harmful *(negative)* transfer is most likely when two skills or activities appear to be the same but differ in important elements *(tennis smash - badminton smash, where the firm wrist in tennis is completely opposite to the supple flick of the wrist used in badminton)*.

◆ No transfer occurs when the skills or activities are not related in any way *(front crawl swimming stroke - throwing the javelin)*.

When you are trying to learn a new skill or activity don't assume that helpful transfer will happen. Always try to avoid the harmful transfer effect by listening to your teacher and focussing on the practice drill.

Guidance & Help

You can be helped in several ways, for example by visual, verbal, and manual guidance.

Visual guidance

When you are practising, coaches and teachers try to help you by showing you what to do. This is called visual guidance. They could show you a video, a picture, or demonstrate the skill.

Verbal guidance

They could try to explain to you what you have to do, or what to improve on. This is called verbal guidance.

Manual guidance

They could also try to help you perform the movement by supporting you, or using some piece of equipment like a swimming float. This is called manual or mechanical guidance.

These guidance methods are basic tools which teachers need to keep 'sharp and effective', but they have to be adapted to suit the learner. They can all help to improve performance by helping you learn the physical movement and prepare yourself better mentally.

Verbal and manual guidance are frequently used together.

3.2 Motivation - Do You Really Want to Do It?

◆ How much do you want to learn a physical activity?
◆ How much effort are you prepared to put into your programme?
◆ How hard are you prepared to work?
◆ How much are you prepared to sacrifice to succeed?
◆ Can you stick at it?

Motivational Level

The answers to these questions reveal your motivational level. Motivation is a very broad term which involves a sense of purpose, commitment, and determination. It affects the intensity of feeling which an individual brings to a situation. Intensity of feeling is also called arousal. Motivation involves a general level of arousal to action, which is focussed and sustained. The 'Inverted U' theory relates levels of arousal to the quality of performance.

Inverted U theory

In this theory, arousal level increases to an optimum point, at which you are performing at your very best *(psyching up)*. Past this point you begin to lose control, and your performance gets worse as you are trying too hard. Some people only reach their optimum arousal in serious competition or performance, whilst others are too easily aroused, and pass their optimum level in competition or performance *(psyching out)*.

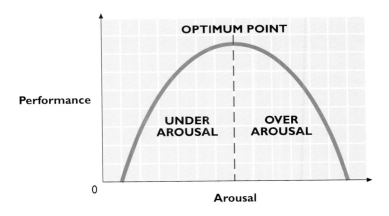

It is important to remain in control and not to 'psyche out'. When you begin to worry, or get anxious, you begin to doubt yourself and performance declines *(see Personality and Performance: p.47)*. Loss of self-confidence is a major problem when people feel under pressure. Arousal should be controlled, if you are to benefit fully from it. Preparing yourself mentally in the right way, remaining focussed and in control during your performance is very important.

Over arousal can interfere with performance, especially skills, like taking a football penalty kick.

Source of Motivation

Intrinsic motivation

Sometimes the source of motivation comes from inside you. It is based on your enjoyment of the activity in which you are taking part for its own sake. This is called intrinsic motivation. This is the best type of motivation, and the longest lasting. All performers need this to stay involved in an activity for a long period of time.

Extrinsic motivation

Sometimes the main source of motivation comes from the external rewards that an activity can bring, such as cups, medals, money, or even praise. This is called extrinsic motivation. This type of motivation uses incentives to keep people interested. Governing body awards are used for this purpose. Incentives need to be matched with individual ability, and must be valued by the performer if they are to have any effect. They are helpful as long as they reinforce an individual's enjoyment, and do not replace it. If intrinsic motivation is lost, what happens when the rewards end?

All finishers in massed road races usually receive a medal since everyone is a 'winner'.

Extrinsic motivation involves trophies like these.

Intrinsic motivation can bring even greater rewards, such as companionship, feeling of well being, and enjoyment.

3.3 Mental Preparation

Mental preparation is as important as physical preparation for successful performance of a physical activity. If you neglect mental preparation, you will not perform as well as you might.

Goal Setting

Goal setting is a process of setting performance targets, and organising practical ways of achieving these targets. This helps people focus on what has to be done to improve performance. The goals should be set in gradual stages which challenge the individual, but are not beyond reach. This enables the performer to achieve the targets, and as a result develop self-confidence and belief in themselves. This self-confidence helps overcome worry and anxiety about their physical capabilities should they occur.

Goal setting is therefore important in maintaining motivation and in preparing mentally.

Successful Goal Setting

If you have achieved your goals in preparing for an event, you will develop confidence in your ability to cope. The National Coaching Foundation identified the principles of successful goal-setting.

S Specific. Goals should be specific to the activity/skill.
M Measurable. Goals must be able to be measured.
A Agreed. Goals should be agreed between coach and performer.
R Realistic. Goals should be achievable.
T Time-phased. The time periods for the goals are stated.
E Exciting. Goals should challenge the learner.
R Recorded. Goals should be written down.

Performance Based Goals

These are the best type of goals to set. You judge yourself against yourself *(personal best)* or against a part of your performance *(eg. percentage of first serves in)*.

Outcome Goals

Outcome goals are to be avoided. In these you measure yourself against others *(position in a race)* and the achievement of the goal is no longer under your control. It depends upon the performance of others.

Goal Setting as a Training Aid

Goal setting can be used as a training aid to direct and sustain performance. By setting carefully selected goals you can direct your training *(work on specific areas where improvements could be made)* and use a set of 'fine tuning goals' to sustain your performance *(you may reach a point where you cannot improve, but need special targets to keep you at your peak)*.

Setting, organising, and achieving targets are important in mental preparation, in maintaining motivation, in the development of self-confidence, and in developing a health-promoting exercise programme.

Action Box

1 With the help and permission of your teacher, choose a practical activity, and using the SMARTER principles set yourself goals for each week over a period of four weeks.

2 Record your progress.

3 Identify any effect the setting of goals had on your performance.

4 With the permission of your teacher discuss your findings in class. Be realistic in what you are trying to achieve.

Relaxation

Try to stay relaxed before, during, and after your performance. There are several ways of doing this. Concentrating on your goals, controlling your breathing, and running through your performance in your mind, can all help to focus your mind and relax you. This can make you less anxious and more determined. Nervousness is normal as long as you don't become gripped with worry!

Good planning and preparation help to put you in the right frame of mind, and help you relax. Routines are useful in bringing familiarity to the situation, and making you feel more at ease *(eg. the tennis player who bounces the ball three times before serving)*. Develop a set routine, and stick to it on the day of performance, and it will help you relax.

There are specific techniques that you can learn to help you relax if nerves are causing you a performance problem. These take time to learn and have to be practised.

Progressive Muscular Relaxation

This is a technique which allows you to gain precise control over your muscles The muscles are dealt with in six groups - shins and calves, small of the back and stomach, shoulders and arms, thighs and buttocks, chest, face and neck. You lie down, breathe slowly, and first tense and relax a muscle group, concentrating on the sensation produced by its tension and relaxation. You work slowly through each muscle group in this way.

Centering

This is a very common, and relatively simple technique. It is a very old breathing technique, designed to reduce tension. You should stand comfortably, relaxing the upper body muscles. You focus on the abdominal muscles, and their tension and relaxation as you breathe. Take deep, slow breaths using the diaphragm (see p.69). You'll feel the stomach extend. Breathe out slowly, and imagine yourself to be heavier as your muscles relax. Practise for a few minutes each day, and this technique can soon be learned.

The Quiet Place

This is a mental technique which requires you to sit or lay down quietly, close your eyes, breathe slowly, and imagine *(visualise)* a place that you find restful - the Quiet Place. Once imagined, you explore the place and relive its quietness.

These techniques, and others, help you to control your thoughts and feelings. You can then focus on the performance and feel in control, for example in endurance events there is an emphasis on creating a mental plan which involves mental practice, positive thinking, relaxation, and emotional control.

Work with your teachers and coaches to achieve your best. Success isn't just about winning. If you are improving then you are succeeding. Losing isn't failure if you've improved.

GET SMARTER!

With the help of your teacher, try to practise centering.

Don't expect success at first. Practise regularly for a few weeks.

Record your feelings and any progress made.

A quiet moment can help prepare for a performance.

Question Box   ?

From what you have read, try to answer these questions.

1 What are curves of learning?

2 What is distributed practice?

3 What is motivation?

4 What do the initials SMARTER stand for?

KEY WORDS

- Learning
- Cognitive stage
- Associative stage
- Autonomous stage
- Performance
- Parts
- Progressive stages
- Whole
- Whole-Part-Whole Practice
- Massed Practice
- Distributed Practice
- Rest
- Mental Practice
- Transfer of Training
- Visual Guidance
- Verbal Guidance
- Manual or Mechanical Guidance
- Motivation
- Arousal
- Anxiety
- Self-Confidence
- Inverted 'U'
- Intrinsic Motivation
- Extrinsic Motivation
- Goal Setting
- SMARTER
- Relaxation.
- Mental Preparation
- Progressive Muscular Relaxation
- Centering
- Quiet Place

CHECK LIST

✔ Learning is measured through performance.

✔ Curves of learning plot practice sessions against performance.

✔ There are 3 stages of learning.

✔ A skill can be learned in parts or as a whole.

✔ Practice sessions can be massed or distributed.

✔ Mental practice is important.

✔ The three forms of guidance are visual, verbal and manual/mechanical.

✔ Motivation involves commitment and determination.

✔ Arousal involves an intensity of feeling.

✔ Inverted U relates the level of motivation (arousal) to the quality of performance.

✔ Intrinsic motivation is about enjoyment.

✔ Extrinsic motivation is about rewards.

✔ Goal setting can help to motivate performers.

✔ Mental preparation is important.

✔ Setting goals involves the SMARTER principles.

✔ Relaxation techniques can be learned (including centering).

4 PHYSICAL FITNESS

There are many definitions of physical fitness. They all focus on physical factors which are part of your overall health. We could think of physical fitness as the capacity to perform repeated activity with relative success, and enjoyment. This normally involves a measure of the relative efficiency of the heart, blood vessels, lungs, and muscles in carrying out movements. In hard physical activity, the enjoyment involves knowing that you have achieved your aims.

You need to be fit to cope with everyday life and not feel tired all the time. The more you do, the fitter you need to be. As you get older you may not be able to withstand the stresses of life as well as you did when you were younger, and you will need to stay as fit as you can.

Let's identify the components of physical fitness that relate to physical activities.

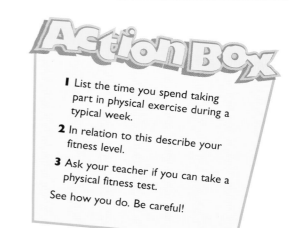

Action Box

1 List the time you spend taking part in physical exercise during a typical week.

2 In relation to this describe your fitness level.

3 Ask your teacher if you can take a physical fitness test.

See how you do. Be careful!

4.1 Components of Physical Fitness

There are various fitness components which influence physical efficiency.

Physical fitness may be considered simply as a combination of two health related components, **Cardiovascular (CV) Fitness** and **Muscular Fitness.**

Cardiovascular (CV) Fitness involves the efficiency of the heart and circulatory system.

Muscular Fitness involves the flexibility, power, endurance, and strength of the skeletal muscles.

The European Test of Physical Fitness *(Eurofit)* suggests a more detailed analysis involving other fitness components.

The importance of health related fitness lasts a lifetime.

Activity Related Physical Fitness	Cardiovascular-respiratory Endurance Muscular Endurance Strength Mobility & Flexibility Body Composition	Health Related Fitness
	Speed Power Agility Balance Coordination	Skill Related Fitness

Modified after the European Test of Physical Fitness *(Eurofit, 1988).*

Exercise machines are good for all ages, can be carefully controlled in a systematic fitness programme, avoid the worst of the weather, and provide women with a safe environment free from worry, and opportunities for those living hectic urban lifestyles.

Harvard step test in progress.

Cardiovascular-Respiratory Endurance

This type of endurance, also known as heart–breathing endurance involves the efficiency of the lungs, heart and blood transport systems, in maintaining the aerobic work which is involved in longer endurance activities. There are many tests for this fitness component.

Harvard Step Test

This test comes in several forms. A commonly used form is the '5 minute test'. The pulse rate is taken at rest. You then have to step up and down 30 times a minute on a 45 cm high bench for 5 minutes. You must start each step with the same foot every time. Your pulse rate is measured at 1 to 1.5 minutes, 2 to 2.5 minutes, and 3 to 3.5 minutes after completing the test. The higher your heart-breathing fitness *(cardiovascular–respiratory fitness)*, the less your heart rate will rise, and the quicker it will return to normal. You are awarded scores depending on the heart rate rise and recovery.

$$\textbf{Fitness score} = \frac{\textbf{Duration of exercise in seconds}}{\textbf{2 x Sum of recovery pulse rates}} \times \textbf{100}$$

Excellent fitness levels exceed a score of 90, average levels are between 65-79, and very poor levels are below 55.

Cooper Test

In this test, you have to run/walk as far as you can in 12 minutes. The distance you cover is compared to standard result tables. An excellent fitness score would involve completion of approximately 1.8 miles *(2.88 kilometres)* for boys and 1.4 miles *(2.24 kilometres)* for girls, in the 15-16 year old age group.

Score Classification for Harvard Step Test

Fitness category	Score (Boys & Girls)
Very poor	below 55
Poor	56 – 64
Average	65 – 79
Good	80 – 89
Excellent	90 or above

Score Classification for Cooper Test

Fitness category	Distance covered in 12 minutes Boys	Girls
Very poor	less than 1.2 miles	less than 1.2 miles
Poor	1.20 – 1.23	1.02 – 1.19
Average	1.24 – 1.53	1.20 – 1.27
Good	1.54 – 1.84	1.28 – 1.42
Excellent	more than 1.84	more than 1.42

To convert to Km. multiply by 1.6

The Cooper test requires motivation and determination, a fit person who is poorly motivated and lacks determination will score lower than they should.

NCF Multistage Fitness Test

This test involves a series of 20 metre shuttle runs at increasing speeds. The speed of each shuttle is dictated by a series of bleeps on an instruction tape. Therefore the test is commonly called the 'bleep' test. Each level demands a greater amount of fitness, that is your maximum ability to absorb, deliver and use oxygen *(VO$_2$ max)*. A standard chart relates the number of shuttles completed to your fitness level.

Without turning boards like these you will achieve a lower score on the NCF Multistage Fitness Test, as you will find it difficult to stop or change direction at the end of each shuttle run.

MULTISTAGE FITNESS TEST
Table of Predicted Maximum Oxygen Uptake Values
Department of Physical Education and Sports Science Loughborough University

Level	Shuttle	Predicted VO$_2$ Max	Notes
6	6	35.0	
9	6	45.2	
12	6	55.4	**Average runner should run 10k** *(6.2 miles)* **in about 42 minutes**
19	6	79.2	**Probable maximum for females**
21	16	88.2	**Close to maximum for male Chris Boardman, cyclist World record holder** *(1997)*

Question Box ?

Describe how you would carry out either:

1 the Harvard step test; or
2 the Cooper test.

Muscular Endurance

Muscular endurance involves your ability to keep movements going when the groups of muscles involved are getting tired, rather than the body as a whole. Simple tests for muscular endurance include completing as many sit-ups or press-ups as you can in one minute.

Sit ups should be performed with knees bent to isolate the action of the abdominal muscles. No sit ups should be performed with the hands behind the head, for fear of damaging the neck.

'Box' press ups may be performed with the knees on the ground. These reduce both the tension on the abdomen and the weight to be pushed up.

Proper form is important to gain maximum benefit.

Sit ups may be performed by reaching only as far as the bent knees, this keeps the tension on the abdominal muscles.

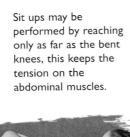

Note the hands on the side of the head, not behind the head!

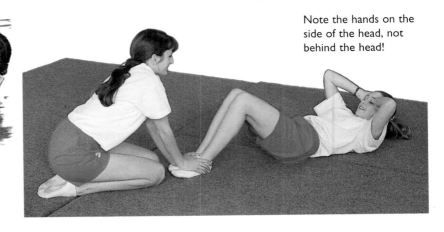

Strength

Strength is the amount of force that you can produce when you contract your muscles. There are two main types.

Static Strength *(Isometric Strength)*

This involves the application of force by muscle groups against an object that does not move. Wrestlers and rugby pack players use this type of strength.

Dynamic Strength *(Isotonic Strength)*

This involves the muscles producing force acting on an object that does move. Most physical activities involve this type of contraction eg. canoeists and rowers use this type of strength.

Grip Dynamometer
measuring grip strength.

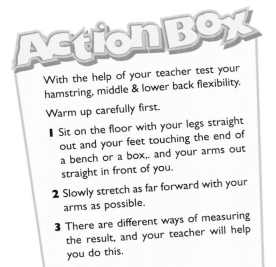

With the help of your teacher test your hamstring, middle & lower back flexibility.

Warm up carefully first.

1 Sit on the floor with your legs straight out and your feet touching the end of a bench or a box,. and your arms out straight in front of you.

2 Slowly stretch as far forward with your arms as possible.

3 There are different ways of measuring the result, and your teacher will help you do this.

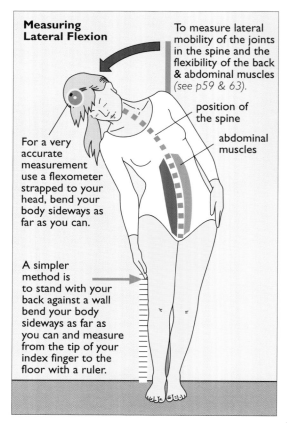

Measuring Lateral Flexion

To measure lateral mobility of the joints in the spine and the flexibility of the back & abdominal muscles (see p59 & 63).

position of the spine

abdominal muscles

For a very accurate measurement use a flexometer strapped to your head, bend your body sideways as far as you can.

A simpler method is to stand with your back against a wall bend your body sideways as far as you can and measure from the tip of your index finger to the floor with a ruler.

Mobility and Flexibility

The range of movement of a joint is determined by both its structure *(shape of the bones & length of the ligaments)* known as its **mobility**, and the physical properties of the muscles *(length & elasticity)* which surround and move it, known as its **flexibility** *(see p.61 & 65)*. Since muscles and joints work together both terms are often used to mean the same thing.

Lack of exercise results in stiffness. Flexibility and mobility can be improved with careful and progressive stretching exercises *(see p.99)*.

Sit and Reach Test

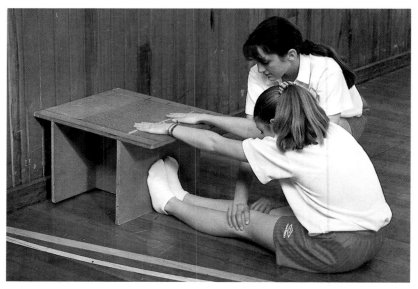

A zero line on the board is level with the soles of the feet. Reaching past this line gives a positive measure of flexibility, and not being able to reach it gives a negative measure. It is important that the legs are kept straight so that it is hamstring flexibility and lower and middle spine joints' mobility that is being measured *(see p.59, 63 & 99)*.

Measurement

Measurement of the range of movement in simple **static** situations *(static flexibility)*, like the sit and reach test, are relatively easy, a basic ruler being the only equipment required, but these and more complex movements can be measured very accurately and consistently using a flexometer. Measurement in extreme **dynamic** situations *(dynamic flexibility)* for the purposes of improving performance, eg. the Fosbury flop high jump, is very difficult and requires sophisticated equipment.

Body Composition

This involves the relative amounts of fat, muscle, bone, and body fluids, etc., and can have a profound effect on performance in different activities, eg. the performance of long distance runners is improved by low body fat, whereas the opposite is true of long distance swimmers, where a high percentage of body fat provides buoyancy, and insulation against heat loss *(see Physique: p.45; & Body Weight: p.46)*.

The Leighton Flexometer is a simple device worked by gravity to record ranges of joint movement.

Speed and Acceleration

Speed of movement is defined by the following equation;

$$\text{speed} = \frac{\text{distance}}{\text{time}}$$ *(metres per second (ms^{-1}) or miles per hour (mph))*

In running, maximum speed is attained by flat out effort over a short distance, as seen in sprinting. The time it takes to reach full speed from a standing start ie. 'speed off the mark' is a measure of acceleration. This is very important in many physical activities. Acceleration can also be involved as a 'change of pace' during a race.

Table of Some Speeds	
International Mens' 100m	**43+ km/h** *(27+ mph)*
Speed Skating *(ice)*	**48+ km/h** *(30+ mph)*
Cyclist *(along level track)*	**78+ km/h** *(49+ mph)*
Greyhound	**66+ km/h** *(41+ mph)*
Racehorse	**69+ km/h** *(43+ mph)*
Cheetah	**112+ km/h** *(70+ mph)*
Man Swimming	**8+ km/h** *(5+ mph)*
Dolphin	**59+ km/h** *(37+ mph)*
Snail *(2 hours to cover 100m)*	**0.05 km/h** *(0.03 mph)*
Swift	**160+ km/h** *(100+ mph)*

Question Box ?

From what you have read, try to answer these questions.

1 What is a simple test for muscular endurance?

2 What is strength?

3 Explain the difference between mobility & flexibility?

4 What is speed?

Power

This is sometimes known as **explosive strength**. It is a combination of speed and strength, and is the rate at which you can work.

$$\text{Power} = \frac{\text{force} \times \text{distance}}{\text{time}} \quad \textit{(measured in watts)}$$

In other words the larger force exerted over the longer distance in the shorter time equals the greater power.

You can only develop maximum power, for a very short period of time. All the strength may be channelled into one explosive act, as in a karate blow or power lifting. Common leg power tests are the Standing Long Jump and the Sargent Jump tests.

In the Standing Long Jump test the distance that can be jumped from a standing two footed take off is measured, this is taken as a measure of explosive leg strength or power. A person's height can affect the distance jumped. This can be allowed for by first marking their height on the mat, and measuring the distance jumped in relation to this. No account is taken of the subject's weight, which also will affect the distance jumped.

In the Sargent Jump test the maximum height a person can stand and reach is marked. The height a person can jump and reach past this mark is a measure of their leg power. Once again no account is taken of the subject's weight, which also will affect the distance jumped.

Weight training, resistance training, and plyometrics, are used to develop power (see *Intermittent Training: p.98*).

Agility

This is the ability to quickly and accurately change the position of your body and/or its parts, with control. Many games require you to stop, start, and alter direction quickly. There are several agility run tests, which normally begin from a lying or sitting position, and involve running around a series of obstacles. Agility is very important for many performers, especially dancers, gymnasts, trampolinists, high jumpers, long jumpers, and pole vaulters.

Sargent Jump Test.

Balance

This is about maintaining the equilibrium *(balanced position)* of your body. You must keep the centre of gravity above its base of support, usually the feet.

Static Balance

This is balance without movement, as in a beam balance.

Dynamic Balance

This is balance whilst moving, for example in squash moving across the court, playing a shot and moving back, or in gymnastics performing a cartwheel.

With the help of your teacher, develop a programme to improve one *(or more)* of the listed fitness components *(see p.35)*.

1 Choose one *(or more)* fitness component that you would like to improve.

2 Identify types of exercise that you could use.

3 Organise a fitness training programme for that component. Specify how long each session will be, and how often. Remember the principles of training, warm-up and warm-down, safety *(see p.95)*.

4 Discuss your ideas with your teacher.

5 Evaluate your programme, and how you could improve it.

Remember, be realistic and practical.

Coordination

This involves your ability to control, and put together movements made by different parts of your body. As you become more skilful, coordination improves, and the eyes, limbs, and any implements *(eg tennis racket)* become more exactly coordinated together.

The components of fitness can be improved through regular exercise and training. This will improve the physical aspects of your performance. To do this, you have to construct a programme of exercises which will challenge you, and that you will stick to, using the Goal Setting principles. Getting physically fit is hard work and it takes time *(see Exercise, Training, and the Principles of Movement: p.92)*.

Under supervision, test your static balance using a balance board.

1 Stand with one foot *(lengthways)* on a 2 cm wide and 20 cm long stick which is positioned on the board.

2 Lift your supporting foot from the ground and record the time you can balance without touching your support foot back on the ground.

THE DRUG DANGERS

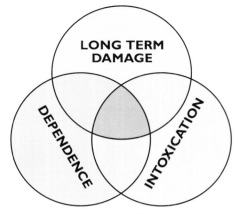

Drugs can be placed into the different zones on this Venn diagram. The very dangerous including most 'hard drugs', solvents, and alcohol occupy the centre zone.

The 4 'L's
the consequences of drug misuse

L is for **LIFE**
irreparable damage to your physical and mental well being

L is for **LOVE**
your personal relationships ruined

L is for **LIVELIHOOD**
your education, employment, and financial security wrecked

L is for **LAW**
all the legal implications, even prison

4.2 Drugs

What is meant by a 'drug'? One definition could be that a drug is a substance, not a food, taken for its effect on the body for medical reasons, or for non medical 'recreational' reasons, particularly for their effects on the nervous system, and for improving sport performance.

Since prehistoric times all societies have used drugs for non medical 'recreational' reasons. Today, we have non medical 'recreational' drugs which are socially acceptable and drugs which are not.

Socially acceptable drugs include caffeine in tea and coffee, and in moderation alcohol. Caffeine has only mild effects, but alcohol has very powerful effects and is widely misused/abused *(increasingly so by teenagers)*. This leads to socially unacceptable behaviour, with serious consequences for the individual, his or her family and society in general.

Smoking tobacco for the drug nicotine, once socially accepted, is now being seen as socially unacceptable as not only does it damage the health of the smoker but also the health of anyone breathing the smoke *(passive smoking)*.

Increasing numbers of drugs with complex effects on the nervous system, are available illegally. The Misuse of Drugs Act places these banned substances into different classes: Class A *(with the highest penalty)* eg. heroin, LSD, cocaine, and Ecstasy; Class B eg. cannabis; and Class C eg. minor tranquillisers.

People take drugs *(or solvents)* for many reasons, including curiosity, boredom, fashion, despair, and pressure from 'friends'. Using drugs, *(or solvents)*, is very dangerous, and mixing drugs is extremely dangerous. They seriously damage your health, can lead to premature death, and sometimes prove fatal the very first time they are used. Drug misuse/abuse also destroy personal relationships. If you work with machinery or drive whilst using drugs you are a real danger to other people as well as yourself. When drugs are injected infection from HIV and/or hepatitis is another danger. Much crime is drug related, due to dealing, and a need to support the habit.

SAY NO TO DRUGS *(National Drugs Helpline 0800 776600)*.

Drugs can affect your fitness, eg. tobacco and alcohol have an adverse affect. Performance improving drugs are discussed in detail later *(see 149 to 151)*.

Tobacco

It is now proved that smoking is bad for the health. Packets of cigarettes carry government health warnings. Some restaurants, cinemas, airlines, etc. ban smoking. The most important area of tobacco control and that showing the most disappointing results is teenage smoking. Very few start smoking as adults, the great majority start in their teens. In 1994 it was estimated that 10% of boys and 13% of girls *(between the age of 11-15)* were regular smokers. Two thirds of teenagers who smoke want to stop smoking. but find it difficult to do so.

Tobacco smoke poisons the body with harmful chemicals such as tar, benzene, carbon monoxide and hydrogen cyanide. Smoking causes cancer, not only of the lungs, but also of many other parts of the body. Smoking will decrease your lung capacity, can cause chest illnesses, decreases the oxygen carrying capacity of the blood, and increases the tendency of the blood to clot internally *(thrombosis)* leading to strokes, coronary heart disease, and leg amputations *(about 2000 amputations each year in the UK)* as a result of blocked circulation. Fitness, health, and performance in physical activities are all negatively affected if you smoke.

Even a non smoker breathing in other people's smoke *(passive smoking)* will have an increased risk of the same illnesses that smokers suffer.

Alcohol

Alcohol is absorbed directly into the blood from the stomach. The more that is drunk, the more damaging are the effects on the body. It slows your reactions, and your responses are therefore slower. It causes muscles to tire, and be more susceptible to cramp. Alcohol can also damage the liver. Moderate drinking *(with meals)* need not be harmful, though alcohol is high in energy and may cause weight to increase. You should not drink alcohol before participating in physical activity. Excessive drinking will negatively affect your fitness, health and performance in physical activities, and can cause violent behaviour and accidents.

CHECK LIST

✔ Physical Fitness is made up of many components, eg. cardiovascular-respiratory endurance, muscular endurance, strength, power, speed, agility, balance, coordination, mobility & flexibility, body composition.

✔ Drugs affect physical fitness, health & performance.

KEYWORDS

- Physical Fitness
- Cardiovascular-Respiratory Endurance
- Muscular Endurance
- Harvard Step Test
- 12 minute Run/Walk Test
- NCF Multi - Stage Fitness Test
- Strength
- Mobility/Flexibility
- Body Composition
- Coordination
- Speed
- Agility
- Drugs
- Tobacco.
- Power
- Balance
- Alcohol

5 PHYSIQUE

Physique or physical build affects performance. It is not always the most important factor, but certain body shapes suit certain activities. Shot–putters tend to be larger and heavier than average. Long distance runners tend to have lighter upper bodies, and longer legs in relation to upper body length. Basketball and volleyball players tend to be taller than average. Gymnasts tend to be compact and muscular. These differences are more obvious at the higher levels of performance.

It has been suggested that some activities would benefit from the introduction of weight categories. Boxing and weight lifting have weight categories; but shot, discus, hammer, and javelin do not. More people might participate and strive for excellence if they did!

Question Box ?

From what you have read, try to answer these questions

1 What is flexibility?

2 What is cardiovascular-respiratory endurance?

3 Describe the NCF Multi-Stage fitness test.

4 What effect do alcohol and tobacco have on the quality of performance in physical activities.

5 What do you think Physical Fitness is?

5.1 Body Typing

A system of body typing or somatotyping, was developed by Sheldon. He measured the body shapes of thousands of people and identified three distinctive and extreme body types. He called these; Endomorph, Mesomorph, and Ectomorph.

Endomorphs - These have a skeletal structure which includes narrow shoulders and wide hips. They also tend to be barrel shaped around the chest, and can build up a lot of fat.

Mesomorphs - These have a skeletal structure which includes broad shoulders and narrower hips. They can develop a lot of muscle mass, and usually have less body fat than endomorphs.

Ectomorphs - These have a skeletal structure which is thin and narrow. They tend to have little fat or bulky muscle mass.

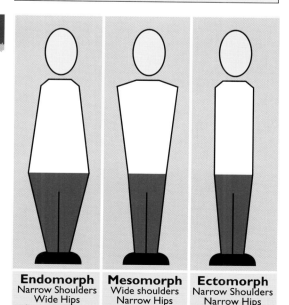

Endomorph
Narrow Shoulders
Wide Hips
Low Muscle to
High Fat Ratio

Mesomorph
Wide shoulders
Narrow Hips
High Muscle to
Low Fat Ratio

Ectomorph
Narrow Shoulders
Narrow Hips
Low Muscle and
Low Fat Mass

It is important to remember that these types are genetically determined. They are based on the basic skeletal structure, which in normal development, is determined by inheritance. Training may change the fat/ muscle ratio, but the basic skeletal structure remains unchanged.

Very few people have these extreme body types.

Measurements taken to determine peoples' body types are converted to three scores, each on a seven point scale. The first number is the endomorph score, the second is the mesomorph score, and the third is the ectomorph score.

The most common body types score in the mid-range of all three scales, eg. 4,3,4 or 3,4,4, etc. as most people are not at the extremes of any of the three scales.

Studies of the body types of those taking part in physical activities usually show more extreme scores than the normal population. This is probably because the nature of the activity, and the training involved, favour those with extreme body types, eg. High jumpers *(1,1,7)*, Sumo wrestlers *(7,1,1)*, and Weight lifters *(1,7,1)*.

5.2 Body Weight

There is a difference between a normal healthy body weight, and body weight required for certain physical activities. Sensible control of body weight, is important not only for participation in physical activities, but also for general health *(see Balanced Diet: p.83)*.

Excess food intake causes fat to be stored in the body, especially under the skin. This fat acts as a heat insulating layer and makes it harder for the body to lose heat. The excess weight makes the heart work harder, and also puts strain on the joints so that movement is more difficult. Energy use is less efficient.

Body fat is measured using Skin-fold Callipers, which pinch up and measure the thickness of a fold of skin at various sites on the surface of the body.

The amount of muscle required for different activities varies. Large amounts of muscle help strength and speed events, but not endurance events where the extra weight is a disadvantage.

Skin-fold Callipers - these must be used only by a properly trained and qualified person to obtain meaningful results.

6 PERSONALITY & PERFORMANCE

Everybody has their own distinctive character, formed as a result of complex factors unique to them and their personal history. Whilst recognising that everybody is an individual, attempts have been made to classify personalities into broad groups on the basis of certain general similarities and differences.

Extroversion/Neuroticism

Eysenck identified the relationship between extroversion *(self assured, outgoing, talkative, social, etc.)*, introversion *(withdrawn, thoughtful)*, stability *(confident, secure)*, and neuroticism *(anxious, insecure, etc.)*. These are shown as two interacting scales or dimensions.

Individuals are given a score based on their answers to questionnaires, which are then placed on these two dimensions. So that one person, for example, could be classified as a stable introvert, and another as a neurotic introvert.

In general, personality testing has not revealed any conclusive evidence relating particular types of personality to specific types of physical activity; but generally it could be said that extroverts prefer more explosive, varied, interactive types of activities such as games; and introverts prefer more individual pursuits requiring long hours of relentless preparation and effort. In relation to neuroticism, performers need to control anxiety and arousal levels to produce their best performance.

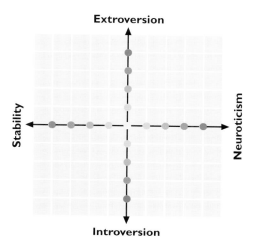

Anxiety

Modern research on the relationship between personality and performance is concentrated more on the analysis of anxiety and its relationship with performance *(see Learning, Motivation, and Mental Preparation: p.25)*.

It is important for anxiety and arousal to be under control and at levels appropriate for the activity. The right level of arousal is needed for performance to be at its best *(see Inverted U theory, p.30)*. Questionnaires have been produced which investigate the type and level of anxiety.

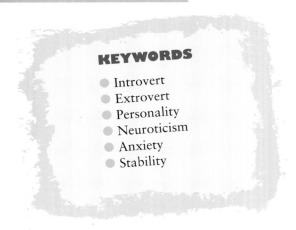

KEYWORDS

● Introvert
● Extrovert
● Personality
● Neuroticism
● Anxiety
● Stability

CHECK LIST

✔ *Personality type can affect performance.*

✔ *Trait anxiety is a relatively fixed part of a person's personality.*

✔ *State anxiety is related to specific situations.*

Trait anxiety

This refers to a persons tendency to become anxious in almost all situations. People who always worry a lot would be said to have a high level of trait anxiety. This type of anxiety is a relatively fixed part of a person's personality, and not easy to change.

State anxiety

This refers to the anxiety you develop and show in specific situations, because of that situation, eg. when climbing a rock face, or when waiting for the start of a race. This type of anxiety can be controlled and adjusted. Teachers and coaches can develop plans to help performers deal with state anxiety using relaxation techniques *(see Relaxation: p.33).*

O.C.E.A.N.

Recent research on personality has re-emphasised five main personality factors. These are openness to experience *(imagination, non-conformity)*, conscientiousness *(dependable, ethical)*, extroversion *(talkative, sociable)*, agreeableness *(warm, good natured)*, and neuroticism *(anxious, insecure)*.

O Openness to experience.
C Conscientiousness.
E Extroversion.
A Agreeableness.
N Neuroticism.

It's likely that future research on personality and performance will concentrate on these factors.

Performing a new activity can be an anxious moment, especially when we are unsure of our physical capabilities, teaching and experience replaces the anxiety with confidence

7 AGE & GENDER

Both your age and your gender *(whether you are female or male)* affect your capacities and therefore your performance in physical activities.

7.1 How Does Age Affect Performance?

Your ability to perform is affected by how old you are. When you are young, your physical capacity improves as you grow and develop. Up to the end of puberty, you improve more due to the fact that you are growing and developing than you do as a result of training. Training has more effect as you become a young adult, and into later life. Sometime around the age of 25, natural physical capacity begins to deteriorate.

Past Your Prime?

Once past your prime, the decrease in physical capacity begins slowly at first, but becomes more and more noticeable as you enter middle and older age. Changes include an increase in the amount of body fat, a gradual drop in the efficiency of the sensory systems, a slowing of reactions, an increase in the brittleness of bones, a reduction in cardiac output *(the amount of blood pumped by the heart per minute)*(see *The Circulatory System*: p.72), a decrease in lung capacity, an increase in resting heart rate, loss of elasticity, greater risk of injuries, and slower powers of recovery.

Things that you think are important, and your attitude, also change as you get older, and this can affect the goals you set yourself, and your motivation. Changes in motivation can have a dramatic effect on participation and performance.

It is normal to change some of the activities you might take part in as you get older. Contact sports and power based activities are often given up in favour of endurance based activities, and non-contact activities.

The maintenance of health as you grow older is important. Part of this involves diet and exercise. If you decrease the amount of exercise that you do, you should adjust your diet or you might put on weight. Generally the changes in the body which occur because of increasing age past your prime, cannot be prevented. Training can, however, help to lessen the effects of age by keeping the body systems as fit as possible. It is important to train appropriately as you get older. If you continue to exercise, and train regularly and correctly throughout your life, there are physical benefits for all parts of the body including the heart, lungs, muscles and joints. Keeping active is important, and physical education should provide a framework for understanding the issues involved in health-promoting exercise.

Development of the ability to catch a ball			
	2 Years old	**5 Years old**	**15 Years old**
General strategy	Virtually nil	Half formed	Complete
Hand movements	Static	Intentional & appropriate but excessive	Directed, smooth, & effective
Timing & coordination	Virtually nil	Effective but slow	Coordinated and unhurried
Eye gaze	On thrower	On thrower ball and hands	On ball
Stance	Rigid	Jerky	Adaptive

7.2 Differences Between the Sexes

There are many differences between the sexes of course, and most of them have an effect on performance.

Boys and Girls

The rate of physical development of young children varies from individual to individual, but girls generally tend to mature physically earlier than boys, and up to a certain age can compete on equal terms.

Men and Women

There are differences in body structure *(anatomy)* and body function *(physiology)* between adult men and women. These affect fitness scores on many tests. However, both sexes can be fit within the limits of their anatomical and physiological differences.

Once both sexes have matured, men tend to be bigger and stronger than women, therefore men tend to produce better performances in activities that involve power, strength and speed. Men also tend to perform better in endurance activities because they have more of the oxygen carrying red blood pigment haemoglobin in their red blood cells, and relatively larger heart and lungs. However, in ultra-endurance events like channel swimming, and very long distance running *(eg. 100+ miles)* women can perform as well as the best of the men.

Women generally have greater flexibility, but both sexes are equally capable of learning skills and strategies.

60

ARM STRENGTH

BOYS

Strength

GIRLS

20

11   Age   17

Question Box ?

From what you have read, answer these questions.

1 What are the main differences between the types of activity in which young and older people might take part?

2 What are the main physiological *(functional)* differences between men and women in relation to physical activities?

Equal Opportunity

Whilst there are differences in structure and body function, both men and women are capable of taking part in all activities. However, even at the Olympic Games, equality of opportunity is still not the case, and women are not allowed to compete in some activities, eg. ice-hockey, water-polo, and weight lifting *(see Women in Sport: p.143)*. There is no reason, other than tradition, why activities based on skill shouldn't be open to both sexes at the same time *(eg. snooker, shooting, archery, etc)*. The emphasis should not be on the difference in performance between the sexes, but rather on the quality of the individual performances. There should be equal opportunity for all to take part in any physical activity they find enjoyable.

CHECK LIST

✔ Age does affect physical performance.

✔ Exercise & training can help to maintain the function of the heart, lungs, muscles & joints.

✔ There are physical differences between the sexes which affect performance.

✔ The emphasis should be on the quality of performance, & the opportunity for all to take part.

KEYWORDS

● Age
● Exercise
● Training
● Health
● Diet
● Gender
● Opportunity

8 EQUIPMENT & SURFACES

The way you perform can be affected by the equipment you use, and the surface you perform on.

8.1 Equipment

Equipment is an important part of many physical activities, and sometimes the need for special equipment can prevent some people from taking part, thus restricting their opportunities.

Technology

Equipment changes all the time as technology influences the design and materials used. Tennis, squash, and badminton rackets, are made of graphite (not wood). Tennis and squash rackets also have larger heads. The 'stringing' of rackets has been improved and new materials are used. These changes have improved the performance and durability of rackets. In pole vaulting fibre glass poles replaced metal ones. The pole vault and high jump landing areas now have specially designed, air filled landing beds, not sand pits. Many Javelin throwers found some difficulty in adjusting to the 'new' javelin which was designed to decrease the length of throws. The 'old' javelin was beginning to reach the track at the other end of the stadia! Boots are lighter and more flexible than before. Running shoes provide more support and protection when running on hard surfaces, because of their ability to help absorb and disperse shock. Cross trainer shoes can be used for several different activities.

The major factors in the design of a running shoe should be the support of the foot, guidance of the footfall, flexibility, and cushioning to help absorb and disperse shock which can be up to 3-5 times normal body weight while running on hard surfaces.

The cushioning part of the shoe *(the midsole and the wedge)* is where there have been many new developments. Originally a single density sheet of EVA *(ethyl vinyl acetate foam)*, developments include varied and multi-density sheets, and gel or air chambers.

A reduction in the hardness of the materials used increases cushioning and flexibility, but decreases stability. Sport shoe design involves a balance between these three characteristics.

Running shoes became a mass fashion accessory in the mid 1970's, resulting in a constant change of styles, many not related to sport use at all.

Safety Equipment

You also have to be aware of safety factors and safety equipment. Many activities have equipment designed to protect you. There are shin pads, helmets, gum shields, padded gloves, shoulder pads, floats, support belts, boxes, goggles and many more. They all reduce the risk of injury which affects training and performance *(see Injury: p.105)*. You have to get used to wearing them. At first they can put you off and affect the way you play. Wearing the right clothing, and feeling comfortable is important.

Heel counter stabilizes the foot minimising rotation and slippage, and helps prevent spraining your ankle *(by turning your foot onto its outer edge)*

Achille's padding

Insole

Padded ankle collar

Padded tongue

Wedge

Lacing

Upper supports the foot

Midsole

Outersole designed for traction *(grip)* and durability *(wear resistance)*

Toe box

Toe cap

8.2 Surfaces

Surfaces vary greatly, and are generally divided between natural surfaces, including grass, water, ice, snow, gravel, clay etc.; and artificial surfaces, including concrete, asphalt, composition, block, rubber, plastic, and wood etc.

Surfaces can be for single activity use (eg artificial ski slopes) or multi-activity use *(eg concrete and 'astroturf')*. Multi-activity use has economic advantages. However, no multi-activity artificial surface has yet been produced that has all the desirable qualities of natural turf.

Artificial surfaces can be used in almost any weather conditions, are long lasting, require less routine maintenance, and provide constant characteristics. Some can change the type of spin, bounce and direction that a ball might otherwise take. The height and speed of rebound of the ball is determined by the 'resilience' of the surface. The speed of roll, the spin of the ball, and the 'footing' of the players, are all determined by the friction between the surface and the object. They all place different stresses and strains on the body, can cause more friction and stress related injuries, and are not accepted for competitions by some Governing Bodies. They are also expensive to build.

Synthetic grass pitches, commonly known as 'astroturf' have a wide variety of characteristics dependent upon the underlying shock pad which covers the concrete or stone base, the length and density of the plastic 'grass', and whether it is water based or sand based. Water based surfaces are sprayed with water before use. This was the original type but is now particularly used for top level hockey. Sand based surfaces, where sand is added, are used more for multi-sport activities and are more economical.

Ski slope surfaces consist of plastic bristles about 45 mm long held vertically by a metal base. Originally PVC, these bristles are now available in PBT which give less friction *(a faster surface)* and is longer lasting. The diamond pattern gives the optimum combination of performance and cost. Too many bristles would give too much friction and high cost, and too few bristles would give too much wear. Artificial slopes require good technique, being less forgiving than natural snow slopes.

If you are used to performing on one type of surface, there can be a dramatic change if you have to adapt suddenly to another. This is also a common cause of injuries. You need to get used to a different type of surface before you perform on it.

Dendix Ski Limited Reg ISO 9002 supply 90% of Ski Slopes in the U.K.

ARTIFICIAL TURF

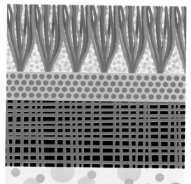

Baspograss and sand

Pre-fabricated Shockpad

Open textured bitumen Macadam

Stone foundation

CHECK LIST

✔ Equipment can affect the way you perform.

✔ Different surfaces can affect the way you perform.

✔ You need to get used to new/different equipment and surfaces before you perform.

KEYWORDS

- Equipment
- Surfaces
- Technology
- Safety

Examination Box One

1 Name one physical skill involved in a game. *(1 Mark)*

2 Identify any two goal-setting principles in SMARTER.

(2 Marks)

3 List three components of physical fitness. *(3 Marks)*

4 Describe the NCF Multi-stage Fitness Test. *(6 Marks)*

5 Five inexperienced table tennis players were each asked to perform 20 table tennis serves into a target area. For the first ten serves, each player was allowed to see where the ball landed *(column A)*. For the second ten serves, each player was asked to turn away immediately after each serve. They did not see where the ball landed. The number of serves landing in the target area were recorded *(column B)*, and the results are shown below.

Player	Column A Results First 10 Serves	Column B Results Second 10 Serves
John	6	2
Gillian	5	1
Steve	4	0
Ashok	7	2
Emile	3	0
Group Total	**25**	**5**

Using the results shown, calculate;

a) Column A mean *(1 Mark)*

b) The % score for Column B where 50 serves = 100%.

(1 Mark)

c) The % difference between the two sets of results.

(1 Mark)

d) Explain the possible reasons for the difference in the two sets of results.

(5 Marks)

(Total Marks = 20)

P.E.
ESSENTIALS
3

Health
Safety
& Training

OBJECTIVES

To enable the reader to understand the following aspects of health, safety, and training;

◆ Health
◆ The Human body and how it works
◆ Balanced diet
◆ Changes in body weight *(mass)*
◆ Posture
◆ Exercise, Training, and the Principles of movement
◆ Safety in P.E.
◆ Injury

Action Box

1 Think about what you understand by the idea of a 'healthy lifestyle'.

2 Describe the ways in which your lifestyle could be changed to improve your health

3 With the permission of your teacher discuss the long term effects of an unhealthy lifestyle.

KEYWORDS

- Health.
- Exercise.
- Hygiene.
- Physical Fitness.
- Health Related Fitness.

Question Box ?

1 What you think being healthy means?

2 What do you think being unhealthy means?

3 Do you think somebody could be fit but unhealthy? Explain your answer.

CHECK LIST

✔ Health is a state of complete physical, mental, & social well-being.

✔ Exercise helps improve your health.

✔ Physical Fitness is the ability to perform muscular work satisfactorily

9 HEALTH

The World Health Organisation describes health as:

"a state of complete physical, mental and social well–being, and not merely the absence of disease or infirmity."

Not many of us can really say we are completely healthy, or have a healthy way of living *(lifestyle)*. By not having a healthy lifestyle, eg. smoking, eating lots of fatty foods and sweets, drinking alcohol, and taking little or no exercise, can lead to poor health. Most people take good health for granted *(especially when you are young)*, you only miss good health when you no longer have it!

It is important to eat a balanced diet and to get enough sleep. Avoid poisoning your body with drugs, including tobacco smoke, alcohol, or air pollution like car exhaust fumes. There is no guarantee that you will always be healthy, but adopting a healthy lifestyle helps.

You need to maintain high standards of personal hygiene with regular washing and dental care at all times. After P.E. you should always take a shower. Hot sweaty clothing and footwear, and communal changing and washing facilities provide ideal conditions for the spread of minor skin infections. Common examples being, viruses *(verucca)*, bacteria *(spots & boils)*, and fungi *(athlete's foot)*. Sensible hygiene will help prevent this type of infection, but no matter how clean you are there is still a risk. Generally skin infections do respond to simple treatments.

Being healthy is not the same as being fit.

The World Health Organisation defines physical fitness as;

"the ability to perform muscular work satisfactorily"

Although health and fitness have different definitions they are very closely related. Generally improving your fitness will improve your health. Fitness which is not so concerned with performance but more to do with your well being is known as **health related fitness**. Fitness which is more concerned with improving your performance is known as **activity related fitness** *(see pages 35-43)*.

10 THE HUMAN BODY & HOW IT WORKS

To understand how the body works *(the study of which is known as physiology)*, you need to study the different body systems which work together.

These systems include the:

◆ skeletal system *(skeleton and muscles)*;
◆ circulatory system *(heart and blood vessels)*;
◆ breathing or respiratory system *(lungs and air tubes)*;
◆ nervous system *(brain, spinal cord, and nerves)*;
◆ hormonal system *(hormone secreting glands)*;
◆ excretory system *(kidneys)*;
◆ digestive and absorptive system *(the gut, associated glands, blood vessels, and liver)*.

Organs - Each of these systems contains various organs eg. the heart in the circulatory system.

Tissues - The organs consist of various tissues working together eg. muscle, nervous and connective tissue in the heart.

Cells - The tissues are made up of large numbers of similar cells. Cells are the basic unit of the body, and are so small that a microscope is needed to see them. An average sized human cell is about 30 thousandths of a millimetre across. About 1000 would cover the tip of a ball point pen. These cells develop from the growth and division of the fertilised human egg. There are about ten million million cells in the human body *(a number it would take you about 400 000 years to count to non-stop!)*.

CELL
pavement epithelial cell

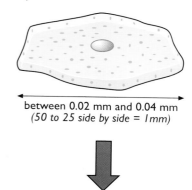

between 0.02 mm and 0.04 mm
(50 to 25 side by side = 1mm)

TISSUE
pavement epithelium tissue
in wall of alveolus

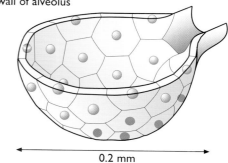

0.2 mm
(5 side by side = 1mm)

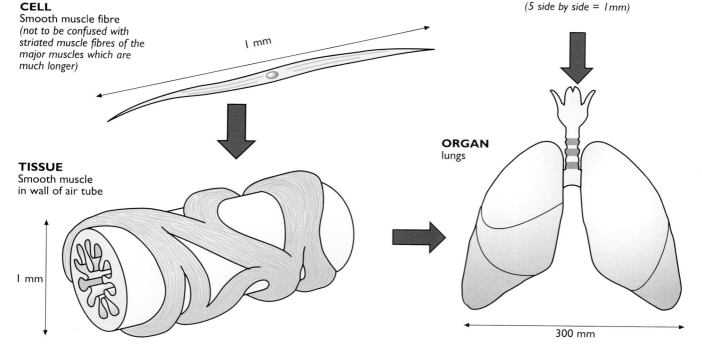

CELL
Smooth muscle fibre
(not to be confused with striated muscle fibres of the major muscles which are much longer)

1 mm

TISSUE
Smooth muscle
in wall of air tube

1 mm

ORGAN
lungs

300 mm

10.1 The Skeletal System

The skeleton is made up of more than 200 bones. The bones are held together by ligaments, their ends are protected from wear by cartilage, and the muscles are connected to them by tendons.

Functions of the Skeleton

The skeleton has many functions.

Protection - Vital organs are protected; eg. the skull protects the brain, eyes and ears; and the ribs protect the heart and lungs.

Support - Vital organs are supported, for example the liver is suspended under the diaphragm *(see p.68)* which is in turn attached to the rib cage, which is attached to the vertebral column.

Movement and Posture - Muscles are attached to the bones of the skeleton. They act together to produce movement, and support the body in a correct position *(posture)*.

Storage of Calcium - Bones contain large amounts of calcium. If there is a shortage of calcium in the diet, calcium is removed from the bones into the blood.

Production of Red and White Blood Cells - Blood cells are made by the red bone marrow, which is found in the centre of some bones.

Types of Bones

Bones can be grouped according to their shape. The shapes of the bones are linked to their different functions.

Long Bones - These are found in the limbs, eg. the humerus, radius, and ulna, in the arms. Their main function is to work as levers, to increase the range of movement caused by the contraction of muscles.

Short Bones - These are found in the wrist and ankle joints, which are very complex with many short bones, which is why ankle and wrist injuries take so long to heal.

Irregular Bones - These have a wide variety of complex shapes, for example the vertebrae of the backbone, and the ribs. The vertebrae of the different regions of the backbone are adapted for different functions. The neck vertebrae allow movements of the head, and this mobility makes them likely to be injured. The vertebrae in the lower back are larger and stronger than those in the neck, and allow less movement as they support the weight of the body. However, despite their strength, lower back problems are common, and can be caused for example by bad lifting technique *(see Safe lifting: p.104)*.

Plate Bones - These are broad, flat bones, designed to protect special areas, for example some of the bones of the cranium protecting the brain; and for the attachment of broad muscles, for example the shoulder blades .

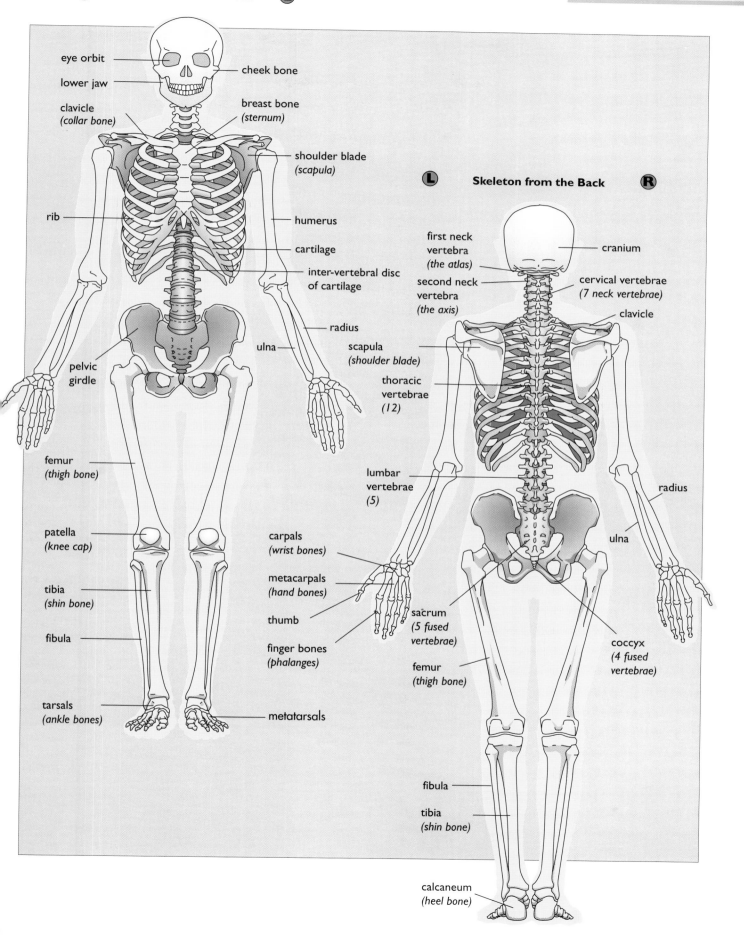

Skeleton from the Front

eye orbit
lower jaw
clavicle
(collar bone)
rib
pelvic
girdle
femur
(thigh bone)
patella
(knee cap)
tibia
(shin bone)
fibula
tarsals
(ankle bones)

cheek bone
breast bone
(sternum)
shoulder blade
(scapula)
humerus
cartilage
inter-vertebral disc
of cartilage
radius
ulna
carpals
(wrist bones)
metacarpals
(hand bones)
thumb
finger bones
(phalanges)
metatarsals

L **Skeleton from the Back** **R**

first neck
vertebra
(the atlas)
second neck
vertebra
(the axis)
scapula
(shoulder blade)
thoracic
vertebrae
(12)
lumbar
vertebrae
(5)
sacrum
(5 fused
vertebrae)
femur
(thigh bone)

cranium
cervical vertebrae
(7 neck vertebrae)
clavicle
radius
ulna
coccyx
(4 fused
vertebrae)

fibula
tibia
(shin bone)

calcaneum
(heel bone)

Question Box ?

Identify these bones

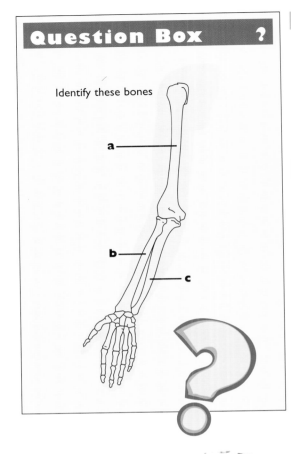

a

b

c

Bone Growth

Before birth, the skeleton is made up of cartilage, which is much softer and more flexible than bone. After birth, the cartilage is gradually replaced by bone tissue. While the 'bones' still contain cartilage they can continue to grow in length. Once the cartilage has been replaced by bone tissue, the bones cannot grow in length any more. They can only continue to grow in thickness, eg. the bones in a tennis player's racket arm get thicker, not longer!

Types of Joint

A joint is where two or more bones meet *(articulate)*. There are three different types of joint found throughout the body.

Immovable Joints

In these the bones are fused together for strength, and no movement occurs between them, for example between the bones of the skull protecting the brain.

Slightly Movable Joints

In these a small amount of movement can occur, eg. the bones at the front of the pelvic girdle are held together by tough fibres that allow some movement, and can be a source of injury in people involved in physical activities

Movable Joints

Most joints are freely movable, and these all share features which prevent friction between the moving bones. One of the main features is the presence of a fluid *(synovial fluid)* between the moving bones. These joints are therefore also called **synovial** joints. The bones are held together by slightly elastic fibres known as ligaments, which allow the bones to move; any damage to the ligaments results in the joint involved losing some of its strength and stability, as is often seen in footballers knees.

There are two main examples of movable synovial joints.

Hinge Joint - The elbows and knees are examples of hinge joints, where movement occurs only in one way *(plane)*.

Ball and Socket Joint - The shoulders and the hips are examples of ball and socket joints, where movement occurs in many directions.

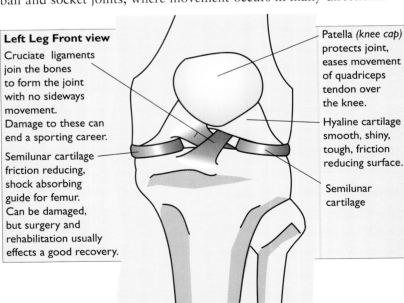

Left Leg Front view

Cruciate ligaments join the bones to form the joint with no sideways movement.
Damage to these can end a sporting career.

Semilunar cartilage friction reducing, shock absorbing guide for femur.
Can be damaged, but surgery and rehabilitation usually effects a good recovery.

Patella *(knee cap)* protects joint, eases movement of quadriceps tendon over the knee.

Hyaline cartilage smooth, shiny, tough, friction reducing surface.

Semilunar cartilage

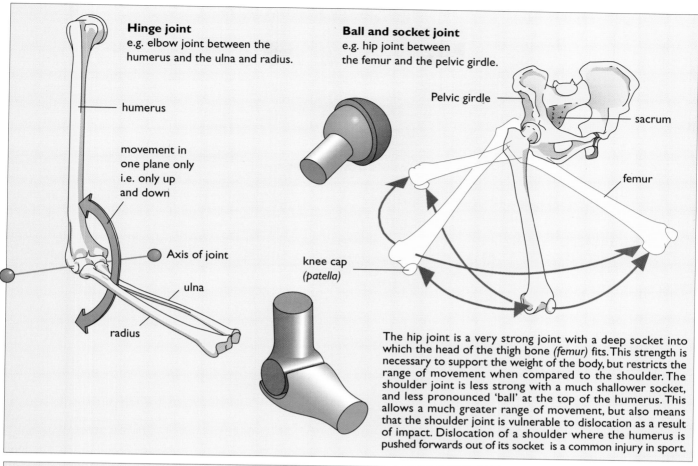

Hinge joint
e.g. elbow joint between the humerus and the ulna and radius.

humerus

movement in one plane only i.e. only up and down

Axis of joint

ulna

radius

Ball and socket joint
e.g. hip joint between the femur and the pelvic girdle.

Pelvic girdle

sacrum

femur

knee cap (*patella*)

The hip joint is a very strong joint with a deep socket into which the head of the thigh bone (*femur*) fits. This strength is necessary to support the weight of the body, but restricts the range of movement when compared to the shoulder. The shoulder joint is less strong with a much shallower socket, and less pronounced 'ball' at the top of the humerus. This allows a much greater range of movement, but also means that the shoulder joint is vulnerable to dislocation as a result of impact. Dislocation of a shoulder where the humerus is pushed forwards out of its socket is a common injury in sport.

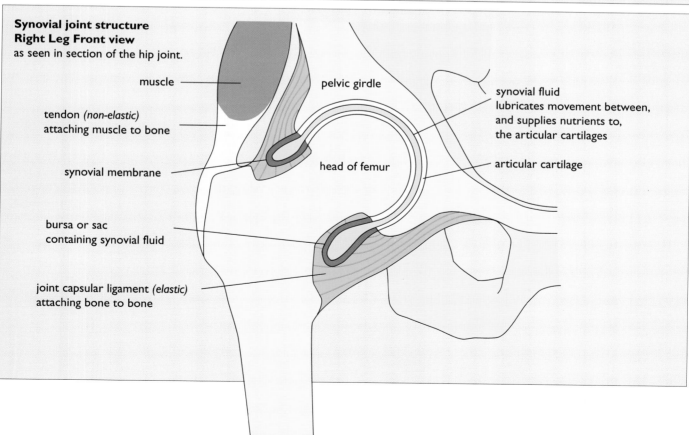

Synovial joint structure
Right Leg Front view
as seen in section of the hip joint.

muscle

tendon (*non-elastic*) attaching muscle to bone

synovial membrane

bursa or sac containing synovial fluid

joint capsular ligament (*elastic*) attaching bone to bone

pelvic girdle

head of femur

synovial fluid lubricates movement between, and supplies nutrients to, the articular cartilages

articular cartilage

10.2 The Muscular System

Muscle is a tissue which can shorten in length *(contract)* to produce movement.

Types of Muscle

There are three main types of muscle in the body, each adapted to a specific way of working.

Involuntary Muscle

Involuntary muscle is not under our conscious control, in other words we cannot make it do what we want. It forms sheets or layers in the walls of hollow structures eg. in the gut, the bladder, and the walls of the blood vessels – especially the arteries. The iris of the eye is composed of involuntary muscle, which results in the pupil of the eye automatically getting larger in the dark, and smaller in the light.

Cardiac Muscle

Cardiac muscle is found only in the heart, and is also not under conscious control. The rate of contraction of the heart can only be altered by the autonomic *(automatic)* nervous system, and by hormones *(eg. adrenaline)*. Cardiac muscle fibres have interconnections between them, which allow for the rapid and co-ordinated contraction and relaxation of all the fibres together, so that the whole heart beats in a rhythmic way.

Cardiac muscle can only carry out respiration with oxygen. It cannot, therefore, develop an 'oxygen debt' by producing lactic acid as a result of anaerobic respiration, like voluntary muscles can. In fact, lactic acid, produced by voluntary muscles of the body which are working anaerobically during exercise, is used by cardiac muscle as a source of energy for its contractions.

Voluntary or Skeletal Muscle

Voluntary or Skeletal muscle is under our conscious control, and we can decide to move in certain ways by contracting various muscles. Voluntary muscle is connected to the skeleton via non-elastic tendons. There are more than 650 skeletal muscles in the body.

Each muscle is a mixture of fast twitch and slow twitch muscle fibres. Fast twitch fibres contract faster than slow twitch, and can work anaerobically without oxygen, using glycogen. Slow twitch fibres work aerobically using fats more than glycogen. Sprinters and games players tend to have a greater proportion of fast twitch fibres, and endurance performers tend to have more slow twitch fibres. The proportion of the fast twitch and slow twitch fibres is genetically fixed, these inherited differences are not affected very much by training.

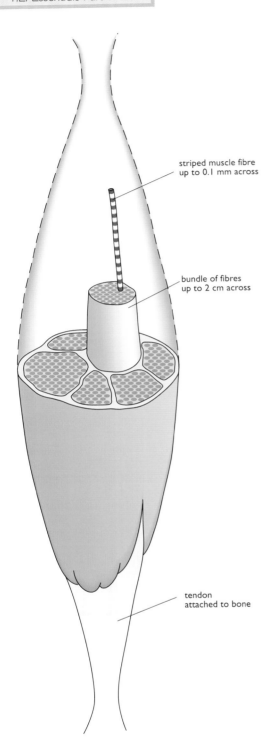

striped muscle fibre
up to 0.1 mm across

bundle of fibres
up to 2 cm across

tendon
attached to bone

A typical voluntary or skeletal muscle, cut away and transparent at the top to show how it is made up of bundles of striped muscle fibres.

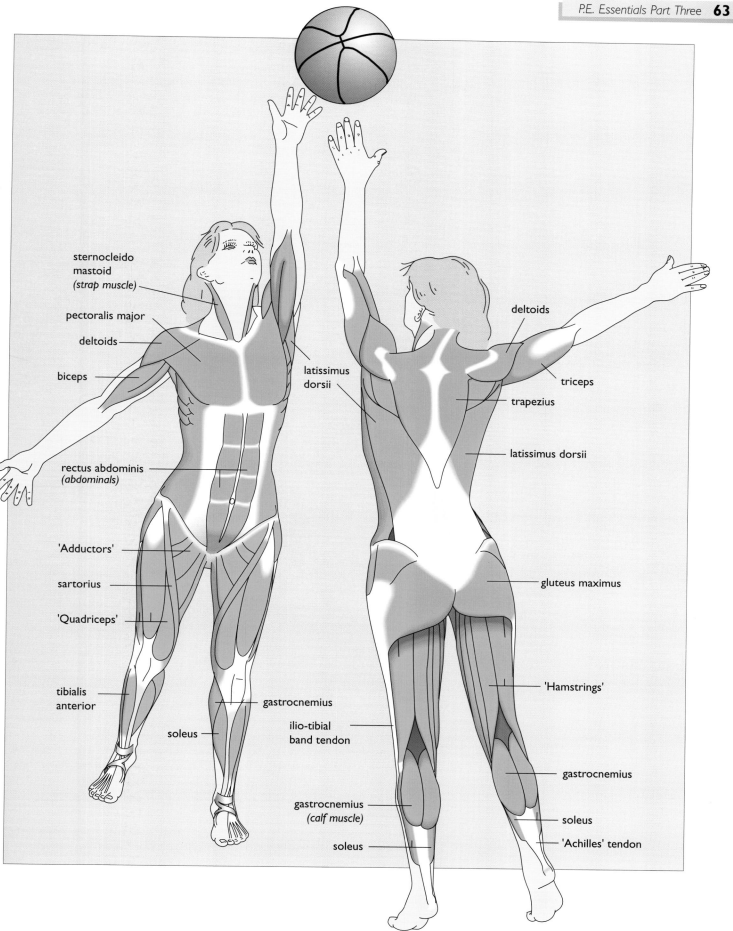

sternocleido
mastoid
(strap muscle)

pectoralis major

deltoids

biceps

latissimus
dorsii

deltoids

triceps

trapezius

latissimus dorsii

rectus abdominis
(abdominals)

'Adductors'

sartorius

'Quadriceps'

gluteus maximus

tibialis
anterior

gastrocnemius

soleus

ilio-tibial
band tendon

'Hamstrings'

gastrocnemius

soleus

'Achilles' tendon

gastrocnemius
(calf muscle)

soleus

Muscles and Bones

When stimulated by motor nerves, skeletal muscles contract, becoming shorter and thicker, and by pulling on the tendons attached to the bones, they produce movement. Tendons can become inflamed by friction, as for example can happen with the Achilles tendon at the heel, when running shoes with badly designed 'heel tabs' are worn *(see p.107).*

Origins and Insertions

Origin - The end of the muscle attached to a relatively immovable bone, as a sort of anchor point, is known as the origin.

Insertion - The other end of the muscle attached to the bone to be moved, is known as the insertion.

For example the biceps muscle bends or flexes the arm at the elbow. The biceps is attached to the shoulder blade which acts as the anchor point *(origin)*, and to the radius bone which is the bone being moved *(insertion)*.

Antagonistic Pairs

Once it has contracted, a muscle cannot restretch itself. Therefore muscles are arranged in opposing or antagonistic pairs, where the contraction of one muscle will restretch the other. This can be seen in the legs and the arms, where there are sets of flexors *('benders')* and extensors *('straighteners')*.

(Other muscles called stabilisers, hold joints firm if necessary eg. holding the wrist firm during a tennis stroke).

Muscle Tone

Muscles are seldom totally relaxed. They retain a certain amount of tension or 'muscle tone'. Muscle tone is important in maintaining the posture of the body.

Study the picture above and try and follow what the major muscles in the leg are doing. A muscle can only contract or relax, but it can be trying to contract while still being stretched longer *(see p.65)*.

1 Quadriceps on front of thighs contract straightening the legs on take off. Antagonistic 'Hamstrings' relax, also calf muscles contract pushing foot up onto toes.

2 'Hamstrings' contract kicking heels up clearing feet off the ground, antagonistic quadriceps relax.

3 Quadriceps in eccentric contraction on landing ie. contracting while being stretched by the weight of the body, in effect slowing the landing.

Question Box ?

Identify muscles a, b, and c in the diagram of the back view of the leg.

a

b

c

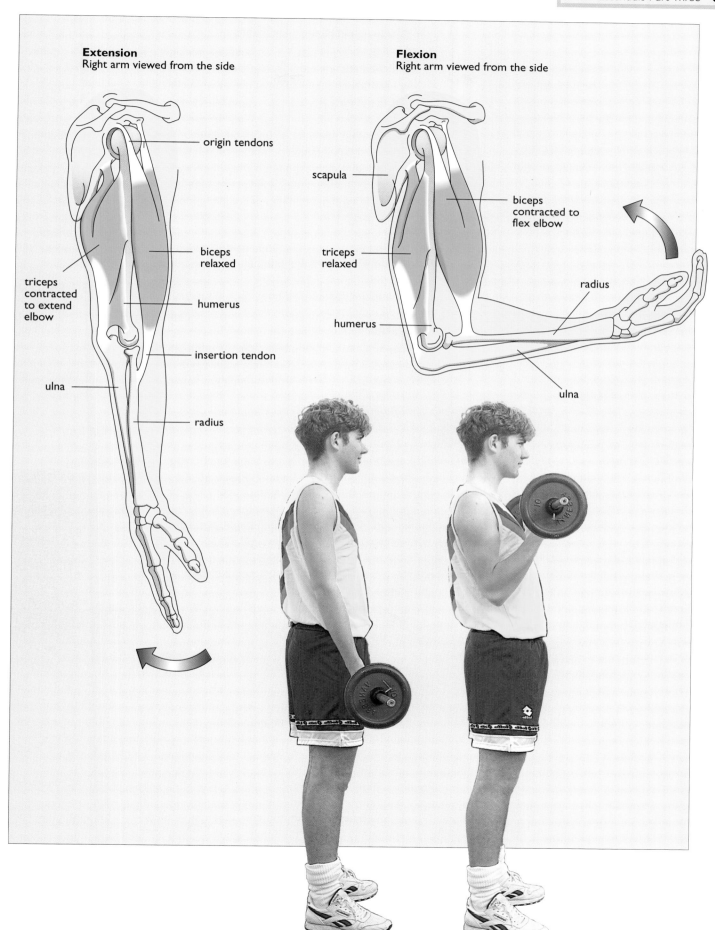

Extension
Right arm viewed from the side

origin tendons

biceps
relaxed

humerus

insertion tendon

ulna

radius

triceps
contracted
to extend
elbow

Flexion
Right arm viewed from the side

scapula

biceps
contracted to
flex elbow

triceps
relaxed

humerus

radius

ulna

The arms being used as
a simple lever

Types of Muscle Action

All muscles contract, and develop tension. However, the type of
resistance the muscles meet, determines the type of muscle action.
There are two types of muscle action, namely concentric and eccentric.

Concentric Muscle Actions

These are the most common types of contraction. Here the muscle
actually shortens in length as it develops tension. There are two ways
in which this happens.

Isotonic Action - This is when the muscle shortens or contracts freely,
eg. the biceps in the arm contracts when 'curling' a weight.

Isometric Action - This is where the muscle shortens or contracts
only a little before it is stopped from contracting any further by an
immovable resistance, eg. trying to lift a weight you cannot move.

Eccentric Muscle Action

This occurs when the muscle is trying to contract whilst it is actually
being lengthened by stretching, eg. the quadriceps muscles at the front
of the thigh when going downhill.

Cramp

This is an uncontrollable, painful contraction of a whole muscle or
group of muscles, which strikes without warning. It may last for just a
few seconds, or at a lower intensity for several hours. It can happen
during intense exercise, when making a sudden movement, in the heat
when sweating, but also when swimming - especially in cold water, and
even during long periods of inactivity, as for example when lying in
bed. The cause of muscle cramp is not fully understood, salt loss can
bring it on, but there are other unknown factors involved. Cramp is
treated by stretching the muscle*(s)* involved, and by massage.

Bones as Levers

A lever is a structure that transmits a force from an effort to a load, via
a pivot point or fulcrum. If you try to 'lever' up an object with a bar,
the amount of effort needed to move the load would depend on the
length of the lever, and the position of the pivot point.

The arms and legs are long levers which increase the range of
movement produced by the contraction of the muscles. The biceps in
the upper arm can only shorten by about 8 cms, but this results in the
end of the arm moving about 75cms.

This arrangement, where the muscles produce a wide range of
movement of the arms and legs, also means that our skeletal and
muscle systems are working at a mechanical disadvantage.

Mechanical Disadvantage - means that the effort needed to move a
load is greater than the load itself. This is illustrated by the fact that if
you try to perform a biceps curl with a 10 kilogram weight, the biceps
has to exert a force about 7 times greater than this.

Different Types of Levers

Levers are classified into 3 types according to the relative position of the effort, load and pivot; and each type is seen in the body.

1ST - **First Order lever** - the **Pivot** *(fulcrum)* is in the centre.
2ND - **Second Order lever** - the **Load** *(resistance)* is in the centre.
3RD - **Third Order lever** - the **Effort** is in the centre.

1 2 3 = P L E

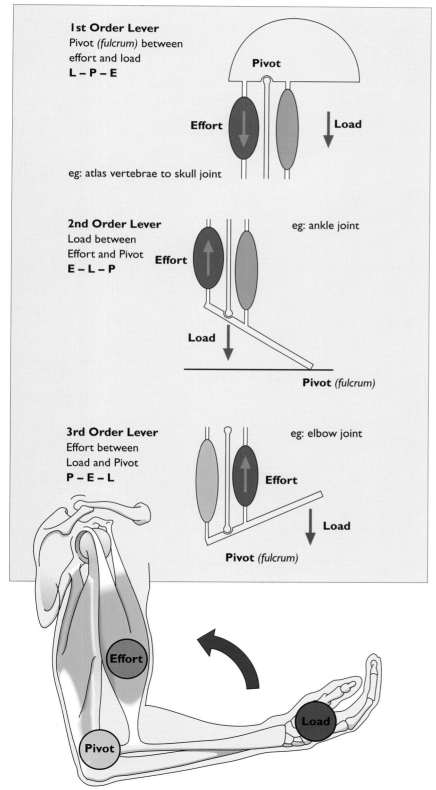

1st Order Lever
Pivot *(fulcrum)* between effort and load
L – P – E

Pivot

Effort   Load

eg: atlas vertebrae to skull joint

2nd Order Lever
Load between Effort and Pivot
E – L – P

eg: ankle joint

Effort

Load

Pivot *(fulcrum)*

3rd Order Lever
Effort between Load and Pivot
P – E – L

eg: elbow joint

Effort

Load

Pivot *(fulcrum)*

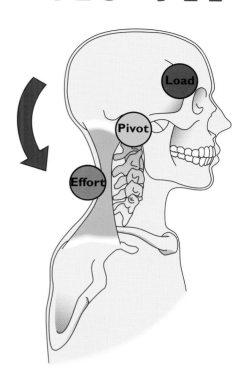

Load

Pivot

Effort

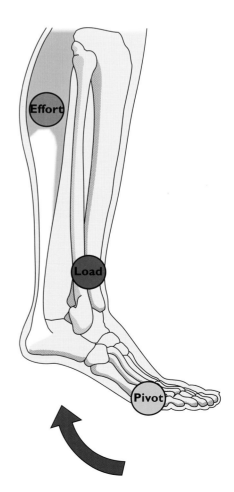

Effort

Load

Pivot

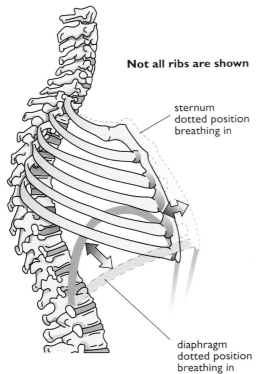

Not all ribs are shown

sternum
dotted position
breathing in

diaphragm
dotted position
breathing in

Muscles Relaxed

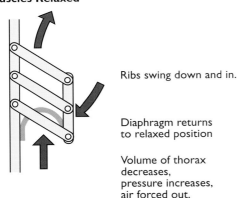

Ribs swing down and in.

Diaphragm returns
to relaxed position

Volume of thorax
decreases,
pressure increases,
air forced out.

Muscles Contracted

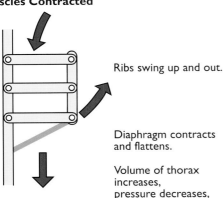

Ribs swing up and out.

Diaphragm contracts
and flattens.

Volume of thorax
increases,
pressure decreases,
external air pressure
forces air in.

10.3 The Breathing System

The breathing system moves air into and out of the lungs, so that oxygen can be taken into the blood stream, and carbon dioxide can be released from the blood stream into the lungs and breathed out.

Structure of the Breathing System

The breathing system consists of two lungs surrounded by membranes, and the system of air tubes supplying the lungs, in the chest cavity *(thorax)*.

The chest cavity is made up of the rib cage and the diaphragm.

The rib cage consists of the ribs attached at the back by movable joints to the vertebrae, and at the front to the breast bone. The ribs are moved by the contractions of the muscles *(inter-costal muscles)* which are positioned between the ribs.

The diaphragm is a sheet of muscle and tendon forming the floor of the chest cavity.

Air tubes lead into the lungs, which are made up of millions of tiny air sacs *(alveoli)*. These are well supplied with blood capillaries, and they are elastic allowing them to increase and decrease in size during breathing.

How it Works

The muscles of the chest cavity contract and relax, and air is moved in and out of the lungs.

Breathing-in
The following actions result in breathing-in:
- the inter-costal muscles contract, moving the ribs up and out, and the diaphragm contracts and flattens;
- this increases the volume of the lungs, and decreases the air pressure inside them;
- the greater air pressure outside forces air into the lungs.

Breathing-out
The following actions result in breathing-out:
- the inter-costal muscles and the diaphragm relax, and they and the lungs recoil by elasticity to their original position;
- these changes result in the volume of the lungs decreasing, and the internal pressure increasing above that of the external air pressure;
- therefore the air is forced out of the lungs.

Exercise makes these breathing muscles stronger, and more efficient.

Control of the Rate of Breathing

The rate of breathing is mainly linked to the level of carbon dioxide in the blood. This is detected by the breathing control centre in the brain which controls the rate of breathing. During exercise the carbon dioxide level increases, which causes an increase in the rate of breathing. Lactic acid produced by the muscles in hard anaerobic exercise, enters the blood, and this also increases the breathing rate. These are the reasons you breathe faster during exercise, not because you are short of oxygen!

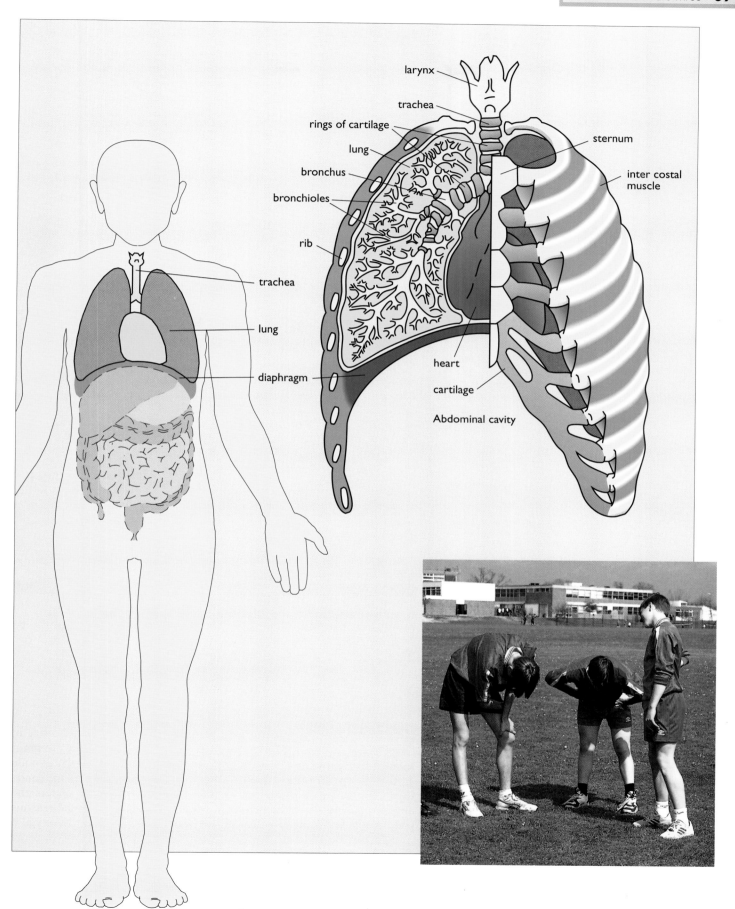

larynx

trachea

rings of cartilage

lung

bronchus

bronchioles

rib

trachea

lung

diaphragm

sternum

inter costal muscle

heart

cartilage

Abdominal cavity

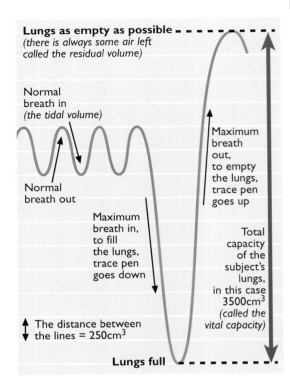

Lungs as empty as possible
(there is always some air left called the residual volume)

Normal breath in *(the tidal volume)*

Normal breath out

Maximum breath in, to fill the lungs, trace pen goes down

Maximum breath out, to empty the lungs, trace pen goes up

Total capacity of the subject's lungs, in this case 3500cm³ *(called the vital capacity)*

The distance between the lines = 250cm³

Lungs full

How Much Air Can be Breathed?

The amount of air that we breathe varies with our demand for oxygen and the amount of carbon dioxide we produce. It is the working muscles which use most of the oxygen and produce most of the carbon dioxide. At rest an adult on average breathes about 16 times a minute. During hard exercise the breathing rate can rise up to 90 times a minute or more, resulting in as much as 200 litres of air being breathed every minute.

Resting Tidal Volume - This is the amount of air breathed in by each breath during quiet breathing at rest, in an adult this is about 500 cm³ air in each breath.

Vital Capacity - The maximum amount of air that can be breathed with the deepest possible breath in and the deepest possible breath out is known as the vital capacity. Some outstanding endurance athletes have very large vital capacities, up to 8 litres.

Residual Volume - No matter how hard you breathe out, it is not possible to completely empty the lungs. The amount of air remaining in them after the deepest possible breath out, is known as the residual volume.

These lung volumes can be measured with a breathing chamber or respirometer. The subject breathes in and out of a chamber, which goes down when the person breathes in, and up when the person breathes out. A pen attached to the chamber records these movements on paper fixed to a revolving drum, to give a trace as shown left.

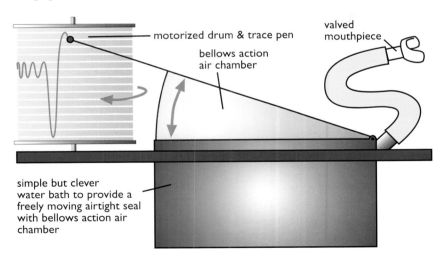

motorized drum & trace pen

valved mouthpiece

bellows action air chamber

simple but clever water bath to provide a freely moving airtight seal with bellows action air chamber

Action Box

Under the supervision of your teacher carry out the following.

1 Before any activity, measure your resting breathing rate per minute, and note it down;

2 Perform the Harvard Step Test (see p.36).

3 Measure your breathing rate per minute until it returns to the resting rate. Record how long this takes. The rate of recovery of breathing rate after exercise is a measure of fitness.

4 When you have completed your health-promoting exercise programme at your school/college/club, test yourself again.

5 Compare the two sets of results. Have you improved?

6 Relate the rate of recovery of your breathing with the rate of recovery of your pulse (see p.74).

Gas Exchange

The air sacs *(alveoli)* are very small, but there are very many of them *(about 300 million in each lung)*, therefore the total surface area is very large *(about 90 m² or the size of a tennis court)*. Each air sac is well supplied with blood, and oxygen diffuses from the air in the alveoli into the blood, and carbon dioxide diffuses out of the blood into the air in the alveoli, over their large surface area.

Oxygen Uptake and Cell Respiration

The oxygen in the air combines with the red blood pigment haemoglobin in the red blood cells, to form oxyhaemoglobin. The oxygen is carried in the blood to all the tissues of the body. The oxygen is used by the cells of the tissues to release energy from food substances absorbed in the diet, eg. glucose. This process of energy release is called **cell respiration**, and it produces carbon dioxide as a waste product.

Glucose + Oxygen → Carbon dioxide + Water + Energy

The volume of oxygen *(V0$_2$)* absorbed from the air in each breath by the blood, depends on the vital capacity and the efficiency of the cardio-vascular system.

Carbon Dioxide Excretion

The carbon dioxide is carried in solution by the blood to the lungs, where it diffuses into the air sacs, and is breathed out. Breathing-out is a type of excretion, as it gets rid of a waste product produced by the body cells.

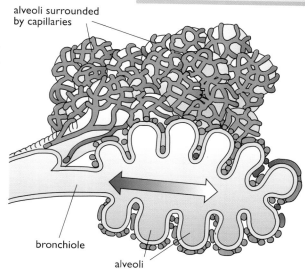

alveoli surrounded by capillaries

bronchiole

alveoli

The Lungs and Pollution

The delicate surface of the air sacs is exposed to a lot of pollution in an industrialised society, eg. dust, and exhaust fumes from traffic. Another major pollutant is tobacco smoke.

Tobacco smoke is a mixture of sooty, tar covered droplets, and hot gases. The smoke particles cover the surface of the lungs interfering with gas exchange. Nicotine, colourless, tasteless, and poisonous is absorbed into the blood stream, causing blood vessels to constrict *(narrow)* resulting in high blood pressure. Carbon monoxide is also absorbed into the blood stream, increasing the 'stickiness' of the blood, resulting in internal blood clots or 'thromboses' *(thromboses in the legs as a result of smoking result in many leg amputations)*. Smoking is also a major factor in heart disease.

The tar contains many cancer causing *(carcinogenic)* compounds, and over the years the tar accumulates in the lungs causing lung cancer Cancer forming chemicals are also absorbed into the cells of the surface of the mouth, throat, and air tubes, and they are carried by the blood to all parts of the body, where they can also cause various cancers.

All the same substances are absorbed by 'passive smoking' of other people's smoke, and cause the same problems and illness in non-smokers. They also pass across the placenta of a pregnant woman and damage the unborn child. The earlier a person starts smoking, the greater is the risk, a fact that makes the problem of teenage smoking particularly serious *(about 450 young people start smoking every day in GB)*. In addition, tobacco smoke is extremely irritating to asthmatics, the number of which are growing all the time, largely, it is suspected as a result of increasing air pollution. Smoking is the largest single cause of preventable death and ill-health in the UK, even though less than 50% of the adult population are smokers *(see Tobacco: p.44)*. There are about 300 deaths a day in the UK as a result of smoking.

Alveoli in cross section

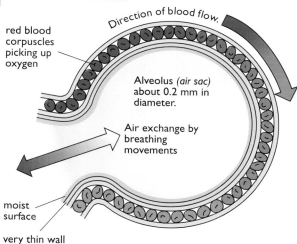

Direction of blood flow.

red blood corpuscles picking up oxygen

Alveolus *(air sac)* about 0.2 mm in diameter.

Air exchange by breathing movements

moist surface

very thin wall of alveolus

Increases shown in bold.

Boys	1982	1996
Age 11	1%	1%
Age 12	2%	2%
Age 13	8%	8%
Age 14	18%	13%
Age 15	24%	**28%**
Total	11%	11%

Girls	1982	1996
Age 11	0%	0%
Age 12	1%	**4%**
Age 13	6%	**11%**
Age 14	14%	**24%**
Age 15	25%	**33%**
Total	11%	**15%**

Percentage of regular cigarette smoking among pupils aged 11 to 15, by age and sex, England, 1982 to 1996.

ONS Smoking among secondary school children 1996

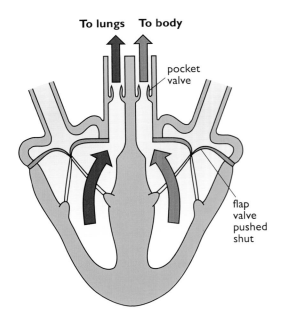

To lungs   To body

pocket valve

flap valve pushed shut

When the heart has filled with blood, the ventricles contract pushing blood up, forcing the flap valves shut *(making the first heart sound)*, and forcing blood up the pulmonary arteries *(to the lungs)*, and aorta *(to the body)*, opening the pocket valves.

Blood falls back down when ventricles relax, closing the pocket valves *(making the second heart sound)* which prevents the blood re-entering the ventricles.

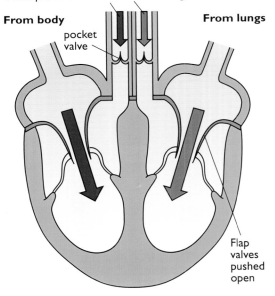

From body   From lungs

pocket valve

Flap valves pushed open

When the heart relaxes it fills with blood, de-oxygenated blood from the bodyon the right side, and oxygenated blood from the lungs on the left side.

10.4 The Circulatory System

The circulatory system consists of the heart, a complete circuit of blood vessels, and the blood.

Function of the Heart

The heart is a muscular pump which pumps the blood around the body. It is in the centre of the chest cavity, tilted slightly to the left side of the body. An untrained heart is about the size of a fist, and weighs less than a pound. It is divided into right and left sides, and the blood passes through the heart twice during each complete circulation of the body.

Cardiac Output

The amount of blood pumped out by the heart in a minute is called the cardiac output. The size of the cardiac output is determined by the number of heart beats per minute, multiplied by the volume of blood pumped out on each contraction or stroke volume.

Cardiac output = heart rate per minute x stroke volume

The cardiac output to the body is increased during exercise as a result of the increase in the heart rate and the stroke volume.

	At Rest	During Exercise
Stroke volume in cm³	75	150
Heart rate b.p.m.	65	200
Cardiac output in cm³ per minute	4875	30 000

The working muscles therefore receive much more blood, and therefore much more oxygen and nutrients. Also heat, carbon dioxide, and lactic acid are carried away from the tissues more quickly.

Effects of Exercise on the Heart

The heart gets stronger as a result of all the extra work it has to do during exercise.

Effects of Endurance Exercise

Endurance exercise *(cross country running and swimming etc.)* results in the heart, especially the ventricles, getting larger with an increased volume and proportionally thicker walls. The ventricles can then pump more blood, more powerfully on each contraction.

The heart gets more efficient as it gets larger, so the resting heart rate slows down. The average resting heart rate per minute is between 70 and 80. Highly trained endurance athletes have resting heart rates as low as 28.

Effects of Power Exercise

Weight lifting and other forms of power work increase the thickness of the ventricle walls, but not the stroke volume. As a result the resting heart rate does not slow down.

Composition and Functions of the Blood

Blood consists of the fluid plasma which contains dissolved substances such as glucose and proteins *(including antibodies and blood clotting proteins)* making 55% of the blood volume; suspended in the plasma are red blood cells, white blood cells and platelets making 45% of the blood volume. The blood transports substances and heat around the body, and defence against infection.

Transport

◆ Oxygen is carried in red blood cells from the lungs to the tissues in combination with the red blood pigment haemoglobin.

At lungs: Oxygen + Haemoglobin → Oxyhaemoglobin
At tissues: Oxyhaemoglobin → Oxygen + Haemoglobin

◆ Carbon dioxide is carried in the plasma from the tissues to the lungs.
◆ Nutrients are transported from the gut to the liver, and from the liver to the tissues in the plasma.
◆ Hormones are transported from glands *(endocrine glands)* to the tissues.
◆ The waste product urea is transported from the liver to the kidneys.
◆ Heat mainly from the muscles and the liver, is transported all around the body.

Fighting Infection

◆ White blood cells produce antibodies and attack any cells or substances that do not belong to the body *(eg. bacteria and viruses)*;
◆ Blood platelets and plasma proteins are involved in blood clotting which helps prevent blood loss and to repair wounds.

BASIC CIRCULATION

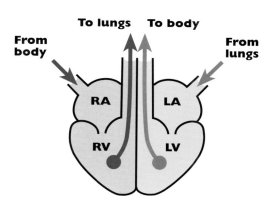

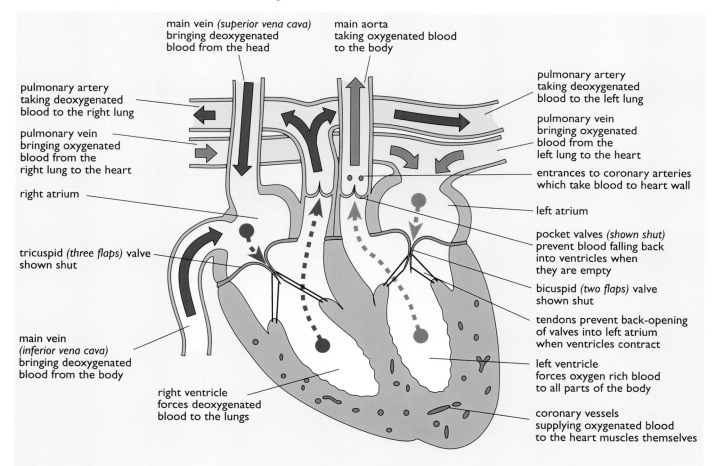

main vein *(superior vena cava)* bringing deoxygenated blood from the head

main aorta taking oxygenated blood to the body

pulmonary artery taking deoxygenated blood to the right lung

pulmonary vein bringing oxygenated blood from the right lung to the heart

right atrium

tricuspid *(three flaps)* valve shown shut

main vein *(inferior vena cava)* bringing deoxygenated blood from the body

right ventricle forces deoxygenated blood to the lungs

pulmonary artery taking deoxygenated blood to the left lung

pulmonary vein bringing oxygenated blood from the left lung to the heart

entrances to coronary arteries which take blood to heart wall

left atrium

pocket valves *(shown shut)* prevent blood falling back into ventricles when they are empty

bicuspid *(two flaps)* valve shown shut

tendons prevent back-opening of valves into left atrium when ventricles contract

left ventricle forces oxygen rich blood to all parts of the body

coronary vessels supplying oxygenated blood to the heart muscles themselves

Action Box

1 With the help of your teacher measure your resting heart rate by taking your pulse at your wrist. Don't use your thumb to measure the pulse. Make sure you are relaxed.

2 Perform the Harvard Step Test (see p.36).

3 Measure your pulse rate per minute until it returns to the resting rate. Record how long this takes. The rate of recovery of pulse rate after exercise is a measure of fitness.

4 When you have completed your health-promoting exercise programme at your school/college/club, test yourself again.

5 Compare the two sets of results. Have you improved?

6 Relate the rate of recovery of your pulse with the rate of recovery of your breathing (see page 70).

The Circulation in Action

The blood vessels help the pumping heart circulate blood around the body.

The Arteries and the Pulse

When the heart contracts, blood is forced into the arteries under high pressure causing them to swell, and when the heart relaxes, the arteries recoil back to their original diameter, helping to pump the blood around the body with an even flow. This rhythmic beat in the arteries is called 'the pulse'. You can feel your pulse where the arteries come close to the surface of the body, eg. on the wrist, the side of the forehead *(the temple)*, the side of the neck etc.

Capillaries

A network of very thin walled blood vessels called capillaries take the blood from the arteries to the tissues of the body, where various exchanges occur between the blood and the cells of the tissues. For example, oxygen, water, nutrients, antibodies, and hormones are diffused from the blood to the tissues; and carbon dioxide is diffused away from the tissues back to the blood. During exercise, blood is moved from the gut, liver, and kidneys, to the working muscles where it is most needed. This is achieved by shutting down capillary beds in the gut, liver and kidneys, and opening extra capillary beds in the working muscles.

Vascularisation

Aerobic exercise involving endurance work like long distance running, results, over a period of time, in the growth of new capillary networks *(vascularisation)* in the active muscles, increasing their potential blood supply, and therefore their oxygen supply during aerobic exercise.

Return of Blood in the Veins

After having passed through the tissues, in the capillaries the blood returns under low pressure in the veins to the right atrium of the heart. Veins have thinner walls than arteries, and have pocket valves along their length which prevent blood flowing back under gravity. Any movement of the body's muscles squeezes the thin walled veins and helps push the blood to the heart. If people stand still too long, gravity can prevent the proper flow of blood to the heart. This can lessen the amount of oxygenated blood reaching the brain, causing the person to faint. It is better to keep moving after a hard run or effort, as this will help the blood flow in the veins to the heart.

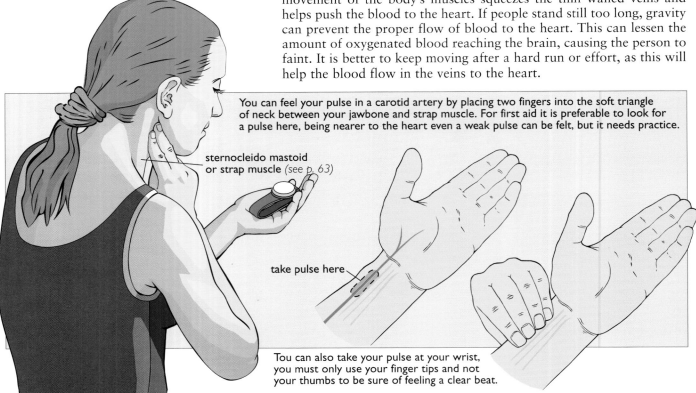

You can feel your pulse in a carotid artery by placing two fingers into the soft triangle of neck between your jawbone and strap muscle. For first aid it is preferable to look for a pulse here, being nearer to the heart even a weak pulse can be felt, but it needs practice.

sternocleido mastoid or strap muscle *(see p. 63)*

take pulse here

Tou can also take your pulse at your wrist, you must only use your finger tips and not your thumbs to be sure of feeling a clear beat.

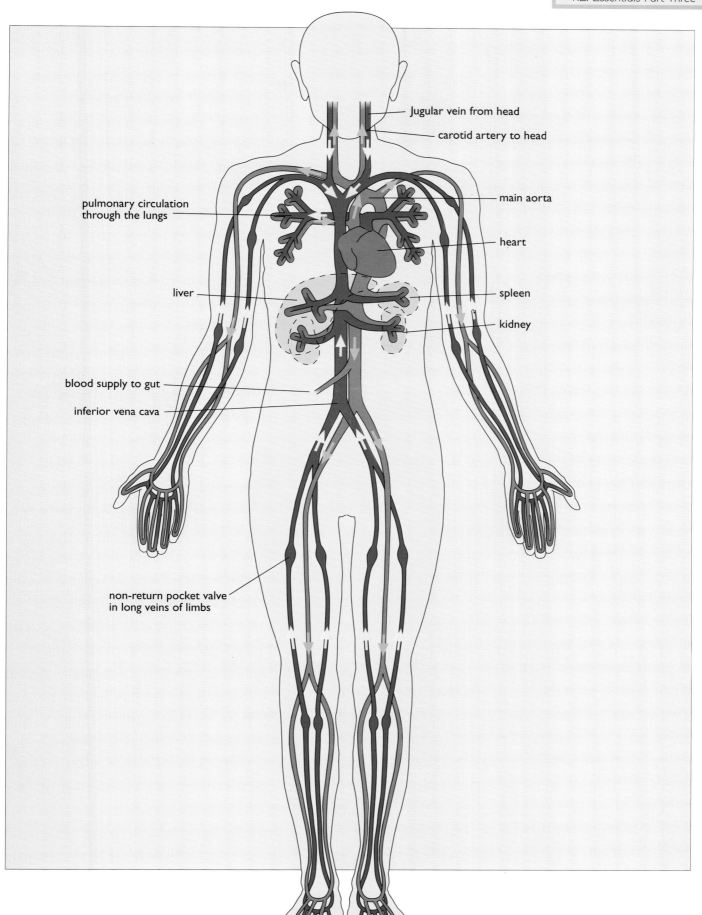

Jugular vein from head

carotid artery to head

main aorta

heart

spleen

kidney

pulmonary circulation
through the lungs

liver

blood supply to gut

inferior vena cava

non-return pocket valve
in long veins of limbs

10.5 The Nervous & Hormonal System

The nervous and hormonal systems work closely together in controlling and coordinating all the body activities, especially during exercise.

The Nervous System

The nervous system consists of the brain, spinal cord, and the nerves which supply all parts of the body. The brain and the spinal cord together make up the Central Nervous System, and the sensory, motor nerves, and sense organs, make up the Peripheral Nervous System.

The Central Nervous System

The brain is the control centre of the entire nervous system, and is where all the incoming *(sensory)* information is processed, and from where the outgoing *(motor)* information originates. The spinal cord carries all the nerve messages *(impulses)* between the body and the brain.

The Peripheral Nervous System

Sensory nerves detect stimuli such as temperature, light, sound, touch etc. and send nervous impulses to the brain. Once the information has been processed, nervous impulses are sent out down motor nerves, to the muscles and glands which carry out the necessary action.

Practising a skill in the right way increases the efficiency of the nervous pathways involved (see *Skill: p.14*).

The Hormonal System

The glands of the body fall into two groups.

Some glands have tubes *(ducts)* through which the substances *(secretions)* that they make either pass out of the body *(eg. tear glands which secrete tears over the surface of the eyes)*, or into a cavity in the body *(eg. digestive glands secreting digestive juices into the gut)*.

The other type of gland does not have ducts and are known as endocrine glands. They produce and release *(secrete)* hormones directly into the blood stream.

Hormones

These are chemicals which have powerful effects on the functioning of the body eg. sex hormones, growth hormone, adrenaline, and insulin. The pituitary gland has been called the 'master' gland of the system, as its hormones control so many other glands. It is connected to, and is under the influence of, the brain.

Adrenaline is important in exercise. It increases the heart rate, and the release of energy, and results in the movement of blood away from the gut to the muscles where it is needed most during exercise.

Insulin helps your tissues to take up, store, and use glucose.

10.6 The Excretory System

Parts of the excretory and reproductive systems are found close together, but they work independently.

The organs of excretion are the kidneys. They filter the blood and maintain the best blood composition. Excess water and poisonous urea are excreted in the urine. During exercise the blood supply to the kidneys is reduced, and the blood is shunted to the working muscles, therefore the kidneys virtually shut down during long bouts of exercise.

Central Nervous System
and Hormonal and Excretory systems

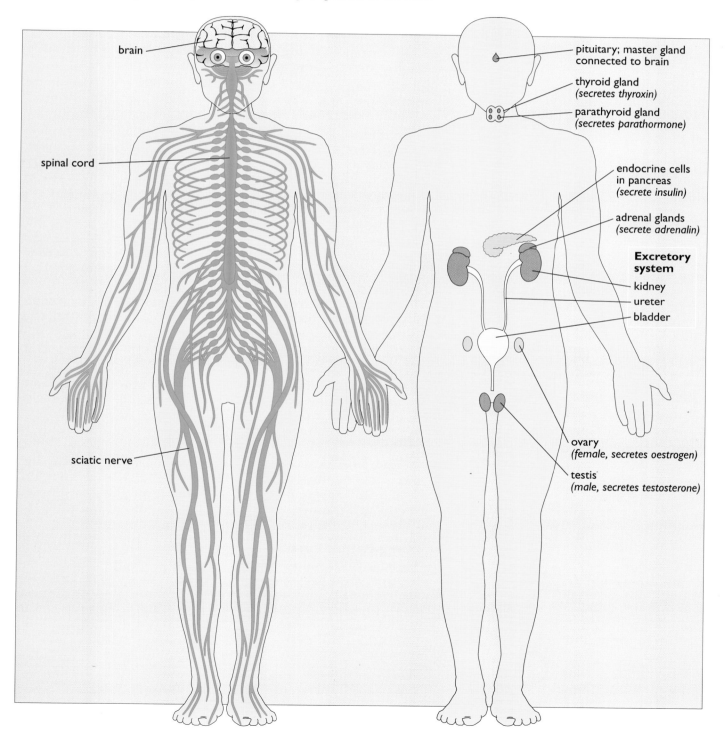

brain

spinal cord

sciatic nerve

pituitary; master gland connected to brain

thyroid gland
(secretes thyroxin)

parathyroid gland
(secretes parathormone)

endocrine cells in pancreas
(secrete insulin)

adrenal glands
(secrete adrenalin)

Excretory system

kidney

ureter

bladder

ovary
(female, secretes oestrogen)

testis
(male, secretes testosterone)

10.7 The Digestive & Absorptive System

The digestive and absorptive system consists of the gut *(alimentary canal)*, salivary glands, the pancreas, the liver, and the associated blood vessels.

Digestion

Digestion is the breakdown of food into simpler molecules, which can be absorbed through the wall of the gut into the bloodstream. Digestion begins in the mouth, which is why food should be thoroughly chewed before swallowing.

Chewing breaks the food into smaller pieces, and mixes it with saliva. Saliva contains a digestive enzyme which begins the digestion of starch. Enzymes are substances which speed up chemical reactions.

After chewing, the food is swallowed into the tube which leads to the stomach. The food is moved down the gut by automatic, rhythmic waves of contraction called peristalsis.

In the stomach the food is mixed with acid to help kill any harmful bacteria. Some digestion takes place, a little water and glucose, *(as well as drugs and alcohol if present)*, may be absorbed directly from the stomach into the bloodstream. The semi-solid food is then released in small amounts into the small intestine, where most of the digestion and absorption occurs. The liver and the pancreas secrete fluids into the small intestine which help digestion and absorption.

The liver - produces bile, which is stored in the gall bladder, and released down the bile duct into the small intestine, where it helps to neutralise the acid coming from the stomach. Bile is also essential for fat digestion.

The pancreas - secretes pancreatic juice into the small intestine. Pancreatic juice contains many digestive enzymes, and also helps to neutralise acid that comes from the stomach.

The digestive process includes the breakdown of:

- Carbohydrates → glucose
- Fats and Oils → fatty acids
- Proteins → amino acids..

Absorption

The end products of digestion, along with minerals, vitamins, and some water, are absorbed into the blood system, and are carried by the blood from the gut to the liver. The remaining undigested food passes into the large intestine, where water is reabsorbed, and eventually the undigested food passes out of the anus as the faeces.

Eating Before Exercise

Digestion and absorption require a large volume of blood in the capillaries of the wall of the gut. If you exercise too soon after eating, blood is moved from the wall of the gut to the working muscles, and food is left undigested in the gut. Try not to exercise too hard until at least 3 hours after eating.

Question Box ?

From what you have read, try to answer these following questions.

1 What does the nervous system consist of?

2 What do endocrine glands produce and release directly into the blood system?

3 What is digestion?

4 What do the kidneys do?

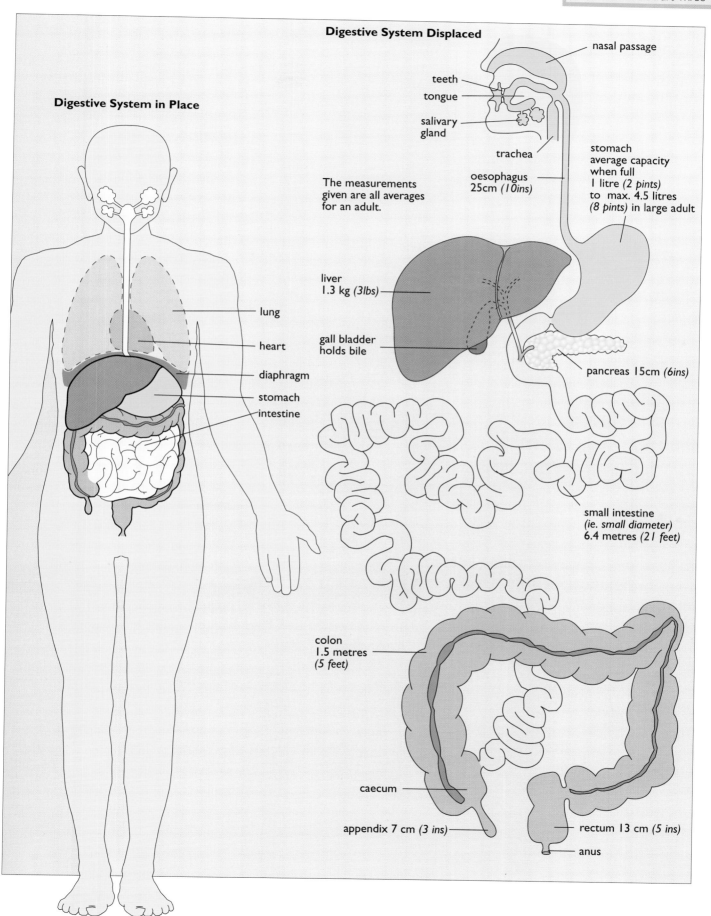

Digestive System in Place

Digestive System Displaced

nasal passage

teeth

tongue

salivary gland

trachea

oesophagus 25cm *(10ins)*

The measurements given are all averages for an adult.

stomach average capacity when full 1 litre *(2 pints)* to max. 4.5 litres *(8 pints)* in large adult

liver 1.3 kg *(3lbs)*

gall bladder holds bile

pancreas 15cm *(6ins)*

lung

heart

diaphragm

stomach

intestine

small intestine *(ie. small diameter)* 6.4 metres *(21 feet)*

colon 1.5 metres *(5 feet)*

caecum

appendix 7 cm *(3 ins)*

rectum 13 cm *(5 ins)*

anus

The Liver

The liver hangs below the diaphragm on the right hand side of the body. The position of the liver suggests an explanation of the 'stitch'. Most people who develop the 'stitch' do so when running, and about 70% develop it on the right hand side. One suggestion therefore is that the 'stitch' is caused by the jarring action of running acting on the liver and diaphragm, causing pain. Cyclists and swimmers with their smoother action rarely get the 'stitch'.

Metabolic functions of the liver

All the blood carrying nutrients absorbed from the gut passes to the liver first before being passing round the rest of the body. The level of nutrients in the blood coming from the gut varies tremendously depending on what you have eaten. The liver adjusts these to the best *(optimum)* levels for the body to function.

It converts excess glucose to the energy storage substances glycogen and fat. Glycogen is stored in the liver and the muscles; and fat is stored all around the body but particularly under the skin. It also converts excess fatty acids to fat. The liver also converts excess amino acids to glucose and the toxic waste product urea. Urea is eventually excreted by the kidneys.

If glucose and fatty acids are in short supply then the liver reverses the processes described above and releases glucose from glycogen stores, and fatty acids from fat stores. The body cannot store proteins so if amino acids are in short supply the liver cannot produce more.

After the liver has adjusted the amounts of glucose, fatty acids, and amino acids to the correct level in the blood, they pass on around the body. The glucose and fatty acids are used by the cells as a source of energy in respiration. The amino acids are used to make the proteins of the body which are necessary for growth and repair of tissues, eg. muscles. However, amino acids can also be used directly as a source of energy if necessary. Very active people should increase their carbohydrate intake to make up for this, so as to 'spare' their amino acids for tissue repair and growth.

10.8 Energy for Exercise

Energy is needed for all the activities of life especially muscle contraction. The food that you eat contains energy rich substances. Once these have been absorbed into the body, energy is released from them by a process known as cellular respiration *(see p.71: Oxygen Uptake and Cell Respiration)*. Some of the energy released is lost as heat, and some is trapped in an energy transferring substance called **ATP** *(Adenosine Tri-Phosphate)*. If there is an excess of energy available, ATP transfers the excess energy into an energy storage substance known as **CP** *(Creatine Phosphate)*. However, the body can only use energy in the form of ATP, therefore the energy in the CP has to be transferred back into ATP before it can be used.

There are three energy systems within cells by which energy is released to be used in exercise. The first two described below do **not** involve oxygen, therefore they are **anaerobic** *(without oxygen)*.

The Alactic Anaerobic Phosphagen System

This is the quickest way of releasing energy for exercise. In this system, energy is first released from the available ATP, which lasts for about 6–8 seconds of flat out effort.

ATP → ADP + P + Energy to be used by the body

(ADP = Adenosine Di-Phosphate: and P = Phosphate)

When the ATP is used, the CP reserve releases its energy to make more ATP. The CP energy store lasts for about another 20 seconds of flat out effort.

CP + ADP → ATP + C *(Creatine)*

In this system of rapid energy release, no lactic acid has been formed *(alactic)*, no oxygen has been used *(anaerobic)*, and both ATP and CP contain phosphate *(phosphagen)*. This is the most used system of energy supply in physical activities involving short, powerful bursts, eg. during games etc.

The Lactic Anaerobic System

This becomes the main system of energy supply if high intensity activity is maintained, and all the ATP and CP is used up. In this case the ATP must be remade using energy released from the breakdown of glucose. As the breathing and circulation systems cannot supply enough oxygen quickly enough to the working muscles, the breakdown of glucose occurs without oxygen *(anaerobic)*. This breakdown is incomplete and only relatively little energy is released, but it is released rapidly.

ADP + P + Energy from the anaerobic → little ATP breakdown of glucose

However, the incomplete breakdown of glucose leads to lactic acid building up in the muscles and blood. This causes heavy breathing and fatigue, and the rate of exercise must slow down, as is seen towards the end of a 400 metres running race.

The Aerobic System

This system operates when the rate of exercise is less intense, eg. when jogging. This process of releasing energy uses oxygen, which reaches the tissues in sufficient amounts in less intense activity. The energy containing substances *(glucose and fatty acids)* are oxidised completely to carbon dioxide and water, and the energy that is released regenerates more ATP. The aerobic system releases much more energy than the other two systems, and is the one which is used most in endurance activities.

ADP + P + Energy from the aerobic → much ATP breakdown of glucose

The aerobic system is also used after intense lactic anaerobic exercise. As the exercise slows due to the build up of lactic acid, the breathing and circulatory systems 'catch up' with the demand for oxygen by the working muscles. The lactic acid, that built up when the intensity of exercise was high, is then broken down *(oxidised)* over a period of time to carbon dioxide and water, with the release of more energy to remake more ATP. A 'warm down' run after intensive activity helps this process by maintaining blood flow to the muscles.

Oxygen Debt

The amount of oxygen taken up after exercise to oxidise the lactic acid is called the 'oxygen debt', and is equal to the amount of oxygen that the individual was short of during exercise. It is to repay the 'oxygen debt' that sprinters for example have to keep breathing heavily for a long time after they have actually stopped running.

Question Box ?

From what you have read, try to answer these questions.

1 What are the five functions of the skeleton?

2 What is the difference between first, second, and third order levers?

3 What are the three types of muscle in the human body?

4 What is meant by concentric muscle action?

5 What is the function of the breathing system?

6 What are the effects of aerobic exercise on the resting heart rate?

7 What are the three energy releasing systems?

KEYWORDS

- Cells
- Skeletal System
- Long Bones
- Short Bones
- Irregular Bones
- Plate Bones
- Immovable Joints
- Slightly Movable Joints
- Movable Joints
- First Order Lever
- Second Order Lever
- Third Order Lever
- Involuntary Muscle
- Cardiac Muscle
- Voluntary Muscle
- Concentric Muscle Action
- Eccentric Muscle Action
- Nervous and Hormonal Systems
- Brain
- Spinal Cord
- Nerves
- ATP & CP
- Alactic Anaerobic Phosphagen System
- Lactic Anaerobic System
- Aerobic System
- Digestive and Absorptive System
- Liver
- Excretory System.
- Breathing System
- Lungs
- Oxygen
- Carbon Dioxide
- Air Sacs
- Haemoglobin
- Glucose
- Circulatory System
- Heart
- Blood Vessels
- Blood
- Cardiac Output
- Stroke Volume
- Heart Rate
- Pulse
- Nutrition
- Carbohydrates
- Diet
- Proteins
- Minerals
- Energy
- Anaerobic
- Fats
- Vitamins
- Fibre
- Aerobic
- Weight.

CHECK LIST

✔ Lots of similar cells together form tissues, some of which form organs, co-ordinated into systems, forming the body.

✔ The functions of the skeletal system are protection, support, movement & posture, calcium storage, & red and white blood cell production.

✔ There are three types of joint: immovable, slightly movable, & movable.

✔ There are three types of lever: First Order, Second Order, & Third Order.

✔ There are three types of muscle: Involuntary, Cardiac, & Voluntary.

✔ Movement is caused by muscles contracting, pulling on tendons attached to bones.

✔ The function of the breathing system is to breathe in air for oxygen, & to breathe out air to get rid of carbon dioxide.

✔ Gas exchange occurs in the lungs.

✔ The circulatory system consists of the heart, a complete circuit of blood vessels, & blood.

✔ The heart is a muscular pump.

✔ The more a healthy heart exercises, the stronger it gets.

✔ $\text{Cardiac output} = \text{stroke volume} \times \text{heart rate}$

✔ The functions of the blood are transportation & fighting infection.

✔ The nervous & hormonal systems work closely together in controlling & coordinating all body activities.

✔ The nervous system is made up of the brain, spinal cord, & nerves.

✔ Excretion is the getting rid of poisonous waste products produced by the body, including urea & carbon dioxide.

✔ The digestive & absorptive system consists of the gut, associated glands, the liver & the pancreas.

✔ The liver adjusts the level of all nutrients in the blood coming from the gut, before the blood passes back into the general circulation & around the body

✔ There are three ways in which energy is released & used in exercise:
1 Alactic Anaerobic Phosphagen System;
2 Lactic Anaerobic System;
3 Aerobic System.

11 BALANCED DIET

We all eat lots of different foods. We're lucky to have the choice. But do we eat the 'right' food in a healthy balanced diet? What is the 'right' food anyway? What's your diet like? What do you eat?

Let's look at some words and what they mean. Nutrition is the science of feeding the body properly with the right nutrients. All the required nutrients are found in their correct amounts in a healthy balanced diet.

A healthy balanced *(vegetarian)* meal. True vegetarians or vegans *(no dairy products, eggs, meat or fish)*, have a much reduced choice of protein sources. Although modern food technology now produces excellent protein foods from fungi *(Quorn)* and Soya beans.

Components of a Balanced Diet

A balanced diet is important in keeping us healthy, providing energy for physical exercise, and maintaining the best body weight. A proper diet, balanced in all the necessary nutrients is essential. Generally speaking a good balanced diet will be enough for you to undertake any type of activity. A balanced diet must contain the right amounts and proportions of carbohydrates, fats, proteins, vitamins, minerals, water, and fibre.

6 CHOICES TO A HEALTHY DIET

1 CHOOSE TO EAT MORE FRUIT & VEG AND WASH or PEEL IT

Try to eat 5 helpings of fruit & veg a day, preferably raw or lightly cooked *(over cooking destroys some nutrients)*. Full of fibre, & nutrients. Takes away hunger pangs, so if you feel like a snack, eat fruit, and if you are still peckish eat more fruit, its good for you. Always peel or wash thoroughly, toxic residues on food due to modern farming methods can build up in the body. Organic produce is free of artificial toxic residues.

2 CHOOSE UN-PROCESSED FOODS

Select whole-grain bread and pastas *(not white)*, muesli style cereals & porridge *(rather than commercial breakfast cereals)*, and fresh, dried or frozen fruit & veg *(not tinned)*. Processed foods lose nutrients *(minerals & vitamins)* in their preparation at the factory, we need these nutrients to stay healthy.

3 CHOOSE TO CUT OUT SUGAR

Without knowing it you maybe eating your own weight in sugar every year! Nearly all commercially prepared foods, soft drinks and alcohol contain 'hidden' sugar *(some do not, & advertise that they are sugar free)*. Biscuits, cake, jam, drinks, most tinned food including tinned meats, sweets, breakfast cereals, and so on all contain sugar. Too many calories leads to an unbalanced diet, therefore choose to reduce the sugar in your diet.

4 CHOOSE TO CUT OUT FAT

Eat less meat, choose lean cuts, choose white meat rather than red, always remove skin or visible fat, choose more fish *(oily fish in the diet helps prevent heart disease)*, avoid sausages, hot dogs, and burgers. Use less butter and margarine, cook with olive oil. Avoid biscuits, crisps, cakes, cream, chocolate, all of which contain high proportions of fat. Choose low fat cheese and skimmed milk *(calcium & protein contents of both are the same as full fat)*. Do not fry foods, it is much better to grill, microwave, steam *(or lightly boil)*, and bake.

5 DRINK MORE FRESH WATER

The body needs water to function properly. Drink small amounts regularly, don't wait until you are thirsty, especially when exercising.

6 CHOOSE TO CUT OUT SALT

To enhance flavours use herbs instead of salt, do not add salt to your meal at the table. Just as with sugar we consume large amounts of 'hidden' salt added to processed foods. Too much salt can lead to an increase in blood pressure.

Carbohydrates

Carbohydrates are the main energy providers and include starch and sugars. Starch is found in many foods, including bread, rice, potatoes and pasta. Only a little sugar is found in our natural foods, most is added to give a sweet taste to various foods. It is healthier to eat more starch and less added sugar. An adequate and regular supply of carbohydrates will maintain blood glucose levels and glycogen stores in the muscles and the liver. Too much will be stored as fat.

A selection of carbohydrate rich foods. The fruit, vegetables and whole grain cereals also supply much 'fibre' commonly known as 'roughage' in the diet.

CARBOHYDRATES
Amount in grams per 100 grams of food

	Starch	Sugar
Apple	0.1	12.0
Orange	0	8.5
Carrots	0	5.5
Potatoes (peeled)	19.0	0.5
Tomatoes	0	3.0
Water cress	0	0.4
White Bread	50.0	1.8
Wholemeal Bread	40.0	2.0
Butter	0	0
Pork (lean)	0	0
Milk	0	6.0
Cheddar Cheese	0	0
Eggs	0	0
Fish (Salmon)	0	0
Nuts	0	0

Fats

Fats contain more energy than carbohydrates, and are found in many foods including butter, margarine, pastry, cakes, and biscuits etc. Fats are especially used by the body in endurance activities when the body is working aerobically. Fats cannot be broken down without oxygen *(anaerobically)*, they need a supply of oxygen to be oxidised to release energy.

An excess of energy rich foods such as carbohydrates and fats will lead to fat being stored in the body, especially under the skin, and around organs like the heart and kidneys. Being overweight is linked with increased risk of high blood pressure, and other associated conditions.

Unsaturated fats - These are thought to be better for health than saturated fats, and are found in oils eg. fish oils and olive oil.

Saturated fats - Too much of these in the diet is thought to contribute to heart problems. The most well known type of these is cholesterol, which is found in animal fats eg. lard, and butter.

FATS
Amount in grams per 100 grams of food

	Unsaturated	Saturated
Apple	0.2	0
Orange	0	0
Carrots	0.2	0.1
Potatoes (peeled)	0.2	0.1
Tomatoes	0.1	0.1
Water cress	0.7	0.3
White Bread	1.5	0.3
Wholemeal Bread	2.0	0.5
Butter	31.0	50.0
Pork (lean)	5.0	5.0
Milk	1.6	2.4
Cheddar Cheese	15.0	20.0
Eggs	7.0	4.0
Fish (Salmon)	10.0	2.0
Nuts	50.0	0

An unhealthy unbalanced meal with an excess of saturated fats.

Proteins

Proteins are found in many foods, including meat, fish, eggs, milk, nuts and cheese. They help build and repair cells of the body, especially muscle fibres. The body cannot store excess protein, therefore protein is needed on a daily basis *(about 1g per kg of body weight)*. Excess protein is broken down and used as an energy source; in this process the poisonous waste product urea is produced, which is excreted by the kidneys.

PROTEIN *Amount in grams per 100 grams of food*	
Apple	0.4
Orange	1.0
Carrots	0.6
Potatoes *(peeled)*	2.0
Tomatoes	0.8
Water cress	3.0
White Bread	8.0
Wholemeal Bread	9.0
Butter	0.5
Pork *(lean)*	20.0
Milk	3.0
Cheddar Cheese	25.0
Eggs	12.5
Fish *(Salmon)*	20.0
Nuts	25.0

A selection of protein rich foods, some of which also contain fats.

VITAMINS
Amount in; (units, A & D), (milligrams, B complex & C) per 100 grams of food

	A	B complex	C	D
Apple	5.0	0.2	5.0	0
Orange	8.0	0.4	5.0	0
Carrots	2000.0	0.8	6.0	0
Potatoes (peeled)	0	1.3	10.0	0
Tomatoes	117.0	0.8	20.0	0
Water cress	500.0	2.3	60.0	0
White Bread	0	2.8	0	0
Wholemeal Bread	0	2.2	0	0
Butter	995.0	0.1	0	1.3
Pork (lean)	0	7.6	0	0
Milk	44.0	1.1	1.0	0.1
Cheddar Cheese	420.0	5.6	0	0.4
Eggs	140.0	4.3	0	1.5
Fish (Salmon)	90.0	11.0	0	12.0
Nuts	0	20.0	0	0

A selection of foods rich in vitamins and minerals.

MINERALS
Amount in milligrams per 100 grams of food

	Calcium	Iron
Apple	4.0	0.3
Orange	41.0	0.3
Carrots	48.0	0.6
Potatoes (peeled)	4.0	0.5
Tomatoes	13.0	0.4
Water cress	222.0	1.6
White Bread	100.0	1.7
Wholemeal Bread	28.0	3.0
Butter	15.0	0.2
Pork (lean)	8.0	0.8
Milk	120.0	0.1
Cheddar Cheese	810.0	0.6
Eggs	54.0	2.1
Fish (Salmon)	93.0	1.4
Nuts	100.0	3.0

Vitamins

These are needed in very small, regular amounts, to maintain health. For example:

◆ Vitamin C is needed for defence against disease, and healthy gums;
◆ Vitamin D is needed for strong bones and teeth.

Some vitamins are water soluble, eg. Vitamin C. They are easily lost from food during cooking. Excess of these in the body are lost in the urine. Therefore there is no point in taking very large amounts of these into the body in the form of too many vitamin tablets.

Some vitamins are fat soluble eg. Vitamins D and A, and any excess in the diet is stored in the body fat. Too much of these in the body can actually be bad for your health.

Minerals

These are simple substances found in all foods. Important minerals include:

◆ calcium which is used in bones and teeth;
◆ iron for haemoglobin.
◆ iodine for correctly functioning thyroid gland.

Vitamins and minerals are found in all foods including milk, cheese, vegetables, fruit, fish, cereals, and eggs.

Water

Water is a basic necessity of life. Without water, you would quickly dehydrate and die. About 66% of an adults body weight, and 80% of a child's body weight, is made up of water. You take in water in the foods that you eat, especially fresh fruit and vegetables, and in what you drink. Water must be replaced during and after physical activity. As you exercise, especially in hot conditions, the body loses water and some dissolved salts. If the activity goes on for a long time you should take in fluids at regular intervals. This will prevent dehydration, and allow the body to keep sweating to control body temperature. Dehydration *(water loss)* is a practical problem for a performer in any activity that goes on for a long time, especially in hot conditions, e.g. tennis matches or a marathon.

A lot of water can be taken indirectly, for example in soft drinks, fruit and vegetables.

FIBRE	
Amount in grams per 100 grams of food	
Apple	2.0
Orange	2.0
Carrots	2.5
Potatoes *(peeled)*	1.3
Tomatoes	1.5
Water cress	1.5
White Bread	2.0
Wholemeal Bread	7.0
Butter	0
Pork *(lean)*	0
Milk	0
Cheddar Cheese	0
Eggs	0
Fish *(Salmon)*	0
Nuts	0

Fibre

Fibre consists of the cellulose cell walls of plant cells *(as does this paper!)*, it is found in many foods including whole grain cereals and bread; and fruit and vegetables. It cannot be digested but is needed for the gut to function properly, and therefore for general health. It gives bulk to the food and helps peristalsis to move the food along the gut, thus keeping the muscles of the gut wall strong. Without enough fibre, food can stay in the gut too long and cause illness. Fibre also makes you feel full, and therefore can help to reduce your appetite.

A selection of foods high in fibre.

Question Box ?

From what you have read, try to answer these questions.

1 What are the components of a healthy diet?

2 Why must energy stores be replaced after exercise?

3 Why must fluid levels be maintained during exercise?

11.1 Energy

Carbohydrates, fats, and proteins are the foods used in providing energy. Carbohydrates are the best because they can release their energy relatively quickly. Fats do so more slowly, and protein is used as a 'last resort'. The rate at which you use energy is known as your metabolic rate. This is affected by your age, whether you are male or female, your physique, your personality type and emotional state, and the type of activity you are involved in.

Energy units - Energy units are called joules. A joule is a very small unit, therefore energy use is normally measured in kilojoules, a kilojoule is a 1000 joules. The older term calorie is still widely used *(1 calorie = 4.2 joules)*. A Calorie written with a **large C** = 1000 calories written with a small c, or 1 kilocalorie.

Energy Needs

The estimated average daily requirements for energy in the UK are:

◆ 15-18 years females 8860 kJ *(2110 kilocalories)*,
◆ 15-18 years males 11570 kJ *(2755 kilocalories)*.

Different activities use different amounts of energy eg.

◆ doing desk work uses about 60 kJ *(14.2 kilocalories)* per hour;
◆ walking uses about 1260 kJ *(300 kilocalories)* per hour;
◆ whilst running and cycling uses about 2520 kJ *(600 kilocalories)* per hour which is equivalent to about 80 grammes of body fat.

Therefore to lose half a kilogramme *(about one pound)* of body fat by exercising, you would have to run or cycle for about 6 hours without taking in any energy.

The energy contained in one medium slice of bread *(340 kJ or 80 kilocalories)* would fuel about 8 minutes of cycling.

Release of Energy During Exercise

Carbohydrates are stored mainly in the liver and the muscles as glycogen. These stores are relatively small, lasting for about two hours of hard exercise. Glycogen breaks down to glucose which is used, with oxygen *(aerobic)* or without oxygen *(anaerobic)*, to release energy.

Aerobic exercise - this involves relatively low intensity exercise over a long span of time, eg. steady walking, running, cycling, or swimming. In this type of exercise, glucose and fats are oxidised with oxygen *(aerobically)* to release much energy. Fats must have oxygen to release energy *(aerobically)*, and can only do so when carbohydrates are being broken down at the same time, *('fats can only burn in the flames of carbohydrates')*. As the stores of carbohydrates are used up, so performance levels decline, and in a long event you find yourself slowing up.

Anaerobic exercise - high intensity exercise, eg. short sharp sprints, does not give the body a chance to supply oxygen to the muscles fast enough for the aerobic breakdown of glucose and fat. Therefore the muscles have to work without oxygen *(anaerobically)*. Only glucose can be broken down without oxygen *(anaerobically)*. When there is not enough oxygen being supplied to the tissues, the glucose, and the glycogen stores which release glucose, are rapidly used up *(see Energy for Exercise: p.80)*. Glycogen stores can be built up by eating a high carbohydrate diet, especially starch containing foods eg. bread, potatoes, bananas, pasta, and rice. After exercise, you must rebuild your glycogen stores quickly by eating foods like this.

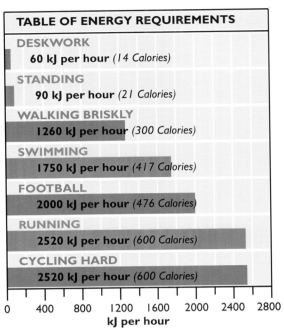

TABLE OF ENERGY REQUIREMENTS

DESKWORK
60 kJ per hour *(14 Calories)*

STANDING
90 kJ per hour *(21 Calories)*

WALKING BRISKLY
1260 kJ per hour *(300 Calories)*

SWIMMING
1750 kJ per hour *(417 Calories)*

FOOTBALL
2000 kJ per hour *(476 Calories)*

RUNNING
2520 kJ per hour *(600 Calories)*

CYCLING HARD
2520 kJ per hour *(600 Calories)*

0   400   800   1200   1600   2000   2400   2800
kJ per hour

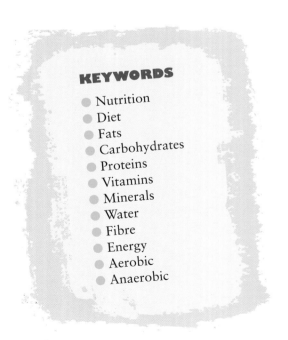

KEYWORDS

● Nutrition
● Diet
● Fats
● Carbohydrates
● Proteins
● Vitamins
● Minerals
● Water
● Fibre
● Energy
● Aerobic
● Anaerobic

12 CHANGES IN BODY WEIGHT
(MASS)

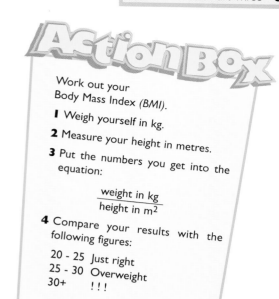

Changes in a person's body weight *(mass)* are mainly caused by changes in the amounts of water, fat, and muscle in the body.

Any changes in the amount of water in the body are normally short lasting, as the body has efficient ways of keeping the amount of water in the body constant, as long as a supply of water is available.

Changes in the amount of fat and muscle take place more slowly. Fat is just a long term energy store, and takes no part in producing movement. Muscles are active, and produce movement using energy in the process. When thinking about body weight and performance, it is important to consider how much is fat, and how much is muscle.

Lean body weight - This is the body weight, minus the weight of fat. This is hard to measure, and the methods used are not very accurate, but it is useful for any performer to be aware of the relative amounts of fat and muscle in their body, as this can affect performance *(see Body Weight p.46)*.

Work out your Body Mass Index *(BMI)*.

1 Weigh yourself in kg.

2 Measure your height in metres.

3 Put the numbers you get into the equation:

$$\frac{\text{weight in kg}}{\text{height in m}^2}$$

4 Compare your results with the following figures:

20 - 25   Just right
25 - 30   Overweight
30+   ! ! !

Losing Weight

There are several ways to lose weight, some are faster than others, but others produce longer lasting results. Let's have a look at some of them.

By sweating - Large amounts of weight can be lost by sweating, for example up to 2 kg per hour *(two litres, about 3.5 pints)* when exercising hard in hot weather. This weight is quickly regained when water is drunk.

By eating less - If you want to lose weight, other than by losing fluids, then the number of joules *(calories)* in the food that you eat must be less than the number of joules *(calories)* you use.

The rate of loss varies depending on your age, sex, activity, and metabolic rate *(the rate at which you use energy)*.

When losing weight, a balanced diet should be maintained. Carbohydrates should still be eaten *(preferably starch)*, with fats being reduced. If you reduce your food intake too dramatically, your metabolic rate slows down so as not to use as much energy. You also lose muscle mass as well as fat, and this further lowers your demand for energy. This occurs each time you diet, and it becomes more and more difficult to lose weight. In this way *"dieting can make you fat"* when you return to normal eating after a diet. Rather than dieting, it is better to change your eating habits slowly so that you can keep it up. You need to enjoy the food you eat.

By exercise - You use more energy while you are active. Also, even after exercise has stopped, the body continues to use energy at a higher level than normal as it recovers. However, exercising can also build up muscle which is heavier than fat, therefore you could become slimmer without actually losing much weight.

Weight can vary from day to day for many reasons, so there is not much point in weighing yourself daily unless you keep records for a careful long term study.

CHECK LIST

✔ *The components of a healthy diet are, fats, proteins, carbohydrates vitamins & minerals, water, and fibre.*

✔ *Physical exercise uses energy containing substances, & causes water loss.*

✔ *To lose weight, joule (calorie) intake must be less than joule (calorie) use.*

✔ *To gain weight, joule (calorie) intake must be more than joule (calorie) use.*

✔ *Beware of the metabolic rate 'compensation' process, whereby dieting can make you fat.*

✔ *Avoid sweating & stopping eating as methods of losing weight.*

Gaining Weight

You could increase your body weight by adding either extra body fat or muscle, or both. If you eat more energy rich substances such as sugars, starch, and fats, and so increase the number of joules *(calories)* you are taking in, above what you are actually using, you will put on extra fat. This extra weight has to be carried by the muscles, and the extra work will lead to some muscle gain, as any extra work above normal will lead to muscle gain.

Protein is essential for building muscle. Enough protein is usually available in a balanced diet, although extra might be needed to meet the demands of heavy physical activity. In order to use protein to build up muscle there must also be sufficient carbohydrates in the diet.

'Making the Weight'

If you take part in an activity which has weight categories like wrestling, boxing, judo, karate, and some rowing events, it can sometimes be difficult to stay below the upper weight limit. Two ways of getting weight off rapidly are to lose fluid *(sweating)*, and to stop eating *(fasting)*. Jockeys and boxers often try to lose weight quickly by sweating in rubber suits or saunas, but this weight is quickly regained when water is next drunk. Also rapid water loss *(dehydration)* can severely affect performance. Over a short period of time, fasting results in the loss of glycogen stores *(your main source of energy in events lasting less than about two hours)*, which will also result in a decrease in your performance. For these reasons you should avoid these methods. Drugs should never be used to 'make the weight' *(see Doping: p.149)*.

13 POSTURE

Posture is about the way all the parts of the body are arranged *(aligned)* together. If any part is out of place *(misaligned)*, it will affect the other parts, and could cause physical pain and injury. Poor posture could be caused by bone or joint defects, or uneven development of muscles. There isn't one postural ideal, other than the general principle that all parts of the body should be properly aligned.

Correct posture looks right, whether you are standing still or moving. You can develop bad postural habits, and these can lead to physical problems in your back, hips, and other parts of your body. Tiredness, poor nutrition, inappropriate clothing, and depression can all contribute to bad posture. Typical postural defects include round shoulders, uneven tilting of the hips, and abnormal curvature of the spine.

Some physical activities involve movements that can lead to poor posture. One example is the breast stroke in swimming, which tends to produce rounded shoulders after many years of intensive training.

It is important to lift correctly *(see Safe Lifting p.104)*; stand, sit, and sleep in ways which involve all the parts of the body being correctly aligned to each other.

If you stand with more weight on one leg than another, you'll probably tilt your hips and put pressure on your back. Very quickly your leg will tire, and you'll want to shift your weight, and your back will ache. If you can achieve good posture you will tend to be less tired, and suffer less aches and pains.

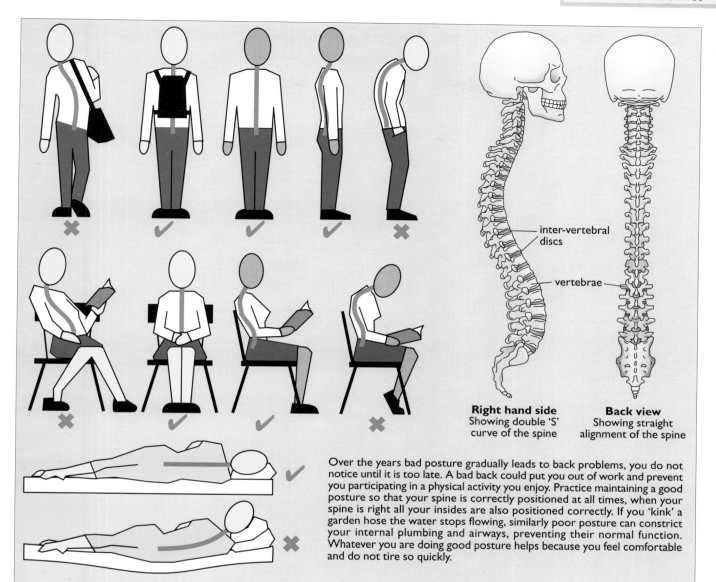

Right hand side
Showing double 'S' curve of the spine

Back view
Showing straight alignment of the spine

inter-vertebral discs

vertebrae

Over the years bad posture gradually leads to back problems, you do not notice until it is too late. A bad back could put you out of work and prevent you participating in a physical activity you enjoy. Practice maintaining a good posture so that your spine is correctly positioned at all times, when your spine is right all your insides are also positioned correctly. If you 'kink' a garden hose the water stops flowing, similarly poor posture can constrict your internal plumbing and airways, preventing their normal function. Whatever you are doing good posture helps because you feel comfortable and do not tire so quickly.

CHECK LIST

✔ Posture is about the way the parts of the body are aligned together.

✔ Some activities can contribute to poor posture.

✔ It is important to:
lift, stand, sit, & sleep correctly.

KEYWORDS
- Posture
- Alignment
- Movement
- Weight

14 EXERCISE, TRAINING & the PRINCIPLES OF MOVEMENT

Health-promoting physical exercise plays an important part in general health. It includes cardiovascular-respiratory *(Heart-Breathing)* endurance, muscular endurance, strength, mobility and flexibility, and body composition *(see Physical fitness: p.35)*. Physical exercise involves exertion of the body.

14.1 Why Exercise?

You have a body that is designed to move and be active. It can be strengthened, or weakened, depending on how you treat it. Instead of becoming overweight and inflexible, you could become stronger and more flexible. This will give you a better quality of life, and you'll be able to do more things without becoming tired all the time. You'll feel better in yourself, and evidence suggests that you have less chance of developing heart disease and high blood pressure. You should be careful not to injure yourself by trying to do too much too soon, or exercising too hard. Always remember to warm up and cool down *(see Injury: p.105)*.

So why do people exercise? Let's list a few of the reasons:

◆ for physical health;
◆ to help lose weight *(fat)*, and gain weight *(muscle)*;
◆ for mental well-being, eg. to relieve stress;
◆ as training for a physical activity;
◆ for satisfaction and enjoyment;
◆ as a recreational activity;
◆ to improve a physical capacity;
◆ to meet others;
◆ for reward;
◆ they feel they ought to.

Question Box ?

From what you have read, try to answer these questions.

1 What do you like most about P.E.?

2 Do you enjoy exercising?

3 Do you think it is important to exercise?

14.2 Exercise & Children

Children grow at different rates. In infancy and early childhood, rapid growth occurs. This is followed by a period of slow steady growth, and a rapid spurt after puberty *(the onset of sexual maturity)* and during adolescence *(the final stages of development)*. The growth rate slows as the adult size is reached.

Strength training has less effect on children before the beginning of the development of sexual maturity *(puberty)* than after it. Their bones are still growing, so weight training is not recommended, as it could lead to bone damage. Circuit training is recommended rather than weight training.

Many of the exercise related differences between boys and girls happen at puberty, and include changes in shoulder width *(wider in boys)* and hip width *(wider in girls)*, the position of the centre of gravity *(higher in boys)*, greater muscle development in boys, and more body fat in girls. All of these affect the mechanics of movement.

Children are unable to supply oxygen to the muscles as quickly as adolescents and adults. The relatively small size of the heart, means that maximum heart rates can be as high as 220, with a resulting loss in efficiency of action.

Also children cannot extract as much oxygen from the air as an adult. They breathe faster and less deeply than adults when they exercise, and this increases water loss from the lungs. Children have a larger skin area compared to their body mass than adults, therefore children lose proportionally more water via sweating. As a result during exercise children can dehydrate more quickly than adults, and should drink regularly.

Compared to adults, children are able to get more of the energy they need aerobically, and can cope with steady activities better than short, intense ones. They are not able to release as much energy anaerobically as adults, and therefore do not accumulate as much lactic acid. After short rests, children typically recover quickly and are ready to try again.

Children tend to be more flexible than adults, and this should be maintained as much as possible.

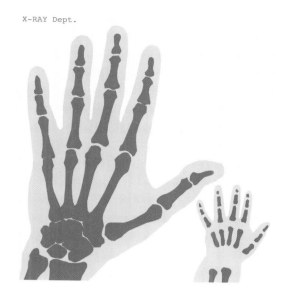

X-RAY Dept.

The skeleton of an infant's hand compared with a young adult. Growing bone which is mainly soft flexible cartilage does not show on an X-ray.

14.3 Effects of Exercise

Exercise can have many beneficial effects.

◆ Aerobic exercise can help reduce body weight if used with an energy controlled diet *(see Balanced Diet: p.83)*.

◆ Aerobic exercise can decrease blood pressure, and reduce the risk of coronary heart disease.

◆ Aerobic exercise lowers the risk of blood clots forming in the arteries, and increases the rate of destruction of any existing blood clots.

◆ Aerobic exercise lowers the resting heart rate.

◆ It can help to maintain the sensitivity of the tissues to the hormone insulin and prevent late onset *(Type II)* diabetes in middle age.

◆ Aerobic exercise causes the growth of new capillary networks *(vascularisation)* in the active muscles, increasing their blood supply, and also the coronary network within the heart muscle.

◆ Exercise can help maintain calcium in bone, and prevent bones from weakening.

◆ Exercise can maintain and increase muscle strength and endurance, and the pulling *(tensile)* strength of ligaments and tendons.

◆ Regular exercise can help you to relax, relieve stress, and improve the quality of your rest and sleep.

◆ Aerobic exercise helps to maintain and improve lung capacity, and help control asthma, and chronic bronchitis.

To maintain these benefits, exercise has to be repeated regularly. If you stop, they can all be lost. This loss is known as the 'reversibility of training' *(see p.96)*.

The health benefits of moderate, properly supervised exercise for the middle-aged and the elderly are becoming increasingly recognised. Doctors are now prescribing supervised exercise programmes for many such patients *(Prescription Exercise)* under the National Health Service.

Many conditions can be helped by exercise. For example some forms of arthritis *(deteriation of the joints)* can be eased through light exercise which maintains mobility of the joints. A Doctor may prescribe swimming, which does not impact the joints, as do many other activities. Various exercises can be prescribed to strengthen muscles where necessary, for example careful supervised workouts on the quadriceps machine.

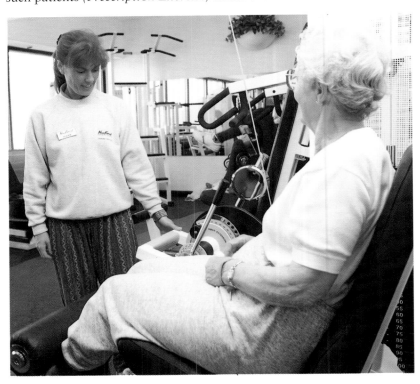

14.4 Principles of Training

Training is a process, based on principles, which tries to improve physical fitness, and motor skills. It involves a balance between work, and rest and recovery. Without proper rest, overtraining and 'burn-out' can occur, causing performance to get worse, and motivation to ultimately go down. People often put a loss of performance down to a lack of training. In many cases it is caused by too much training. Listen to your teacher/coach, and stick to training schedules.

All training should involve a warm-up, and a warm-down *(cool-down)* (see *Injury Prevention: p.106*).

Planning

In planning a training programme you should take account of the **frequency, intensity, time** *(duration)*, and **type** of exercise - **F.I.T.T.**

F Frequency of training sessions should be regular, at least once a week, or two or three times if possible.

I Intensity of the programme should also be related to the capacity of the individual, and the aims of the training programme.

T Time *(duration)* of the session should be related to the capacity of the person; generally, between 15 and 60 minutes is recommended.

T Type of exercise in the programme should be appropriate and relevant to the activity involved.

Training programmes should start with a medical check, for safety reasons.

A training programme should involve long term and short term planning, which establishes an achievable, yet challenging, set of goals. These goals should be specific, measurable, agreed between coach and performer, realistic, time phased, exciting, and recorded (see *Learning, Motivation and Mental Preparation: p.25*).

The use of exercise machines is safer than using free weights, although correct safety procedures are still very important.

Specificity

Training should focus on the physiological and psychological factors special *(specific)* to the activity for which the person is being trained. For example cycling will not help improve your swimming very much.

Progressive Loading *(Overloading)*

Training should put the body functions which are specific to the activity, under progressively increasing stress. This progressive loading, with the right amount of rest periods for recovery, should result in improvement of performance. You could work harder, take part in more training sessions, and/or train for longer periods *(see Planning: p.95)*.

Although the term 'overloading' is widely used it must not be thought of as 'over straining' the body systems, which can of course lead to injury, especially in young people who are still growing.

Mental *(psychological)* factors specific to the activity being trained for can also be developed progressively, in the same way as the physical factors.

Reversibility

If training stops, the improvement will be lost. For example gains in endurance fitness are lost at a rate approximately three times faster than they are achieved in the first place. This loss is known as the 'reversibility of training'. To maintain any improvements, exercise has to be repeated regularly.

Variation

Training should be varied to prevent boredom developing. Otherwise, overuse, loss of concentration and carelessness, can lead to injuries Only safe variation should be used.

14.5 Types of Training

There are a wide variety of types of training, all of which can be adapted to suit particular training programmes.

Continuous Training

This involves the aerobic system, and improves endurance. To do this you could run, dance, swim, cycle etc. In order to keep going at a steady rate, your oxygen demand must be matched by your oxygen uptake.

Target Heart Rate

The intensity of training can be judged from your heart *(pulse)* rate. If you train within certain 'target heart rate training zones' during aerobic exercise, you will make the most efficient gains in aerobic fitness, without starting to work anaerobically and developing an oxygen debt. These levels are dependent on the age, sex, and resting heart rate of the individual.

As a general guide, you can work out your target heart rate training zone by subtracting your age from 220 *(which gives you an estimate of your maximum heart rate)*, and then aiming to keep your heart rate between 60% and 85% of this maximum figure.

Let's work out an example for a person of 45 who wants to exercise for 20 minutes, three times a week, on an exercise machine.

$$\text{Maximum heart rate} = 220 - 45 = 175$$

$$60\% \text{ of } 175 = \frac{175 \times 60}{100} = 105$$

$$85\% \text{ of } 175 = \frac{175 \times 85}{100} = 150 \; \textit{(148.75 rounded up)}$$

Therefore the person should aim for a target heart rate between 105 and 150 beats per minute during exercise.

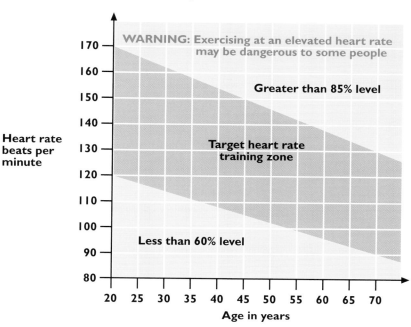

A target heart rate training zone chart showing the band of heart rates within which the most efficient gains in aerobic fitness can be made.

Intermittent Training

Intermittent training involves shorter periods of exercise broken up by various periods of rest or reduced effort. There are various examples of this type of training.

Interval Training

This involves exercising at a certain rate for a certain time *(work interval)*, then resting for a certain period *(rest interval)* in order that you can recover, and then repeating the process again.

Sessions of intervals can be organised into 'sets' with longer rest intervals between them, eg. running a set of 6 x 200 metre efforts with say a minutes jog round recovery between each one, then resting for a longer period of about 10 minutes, before repeating the whole process another two times. This can be represented as [6 x 200] x 3.

You can improve both the aerobic and anaerobic systems in this way. The length of the rest/recovery period depends on how hard you exercise *(intensity)* during the work interval.

Fartlek

This is also known as 'speed play'. It involves 'run as you please' alternate fast and slow efforts over varied terrain, such as grass, sand, flat, hills etc. Unlike interval training, fartlek training does not precisely control the work and rest periods.

Circuit Training

This involves a number of different exercises at 'work stations' which affect the different components of fitness *(eg. strength, muscular endurance etc.)*. The number of 'work station' repetitions, and the rest periods should add up to between 15 to 20 minutes for one complete circuit. You can repeat circuits between 3–6 times depending upon their length.

Strength Training

This can be used to develop strength, power, muscular endurance, and speed. There are many strength training methods.

Weight training - The amount of weight, the repetitions used, and the recovery periods can all be adjusted to progressively load muscles *(see Progressive Loading: p.96)*. Training for strength involves high resistance *(weights)* and few repetitions. Training for muscular endurance involves low resistance and many repetitions.

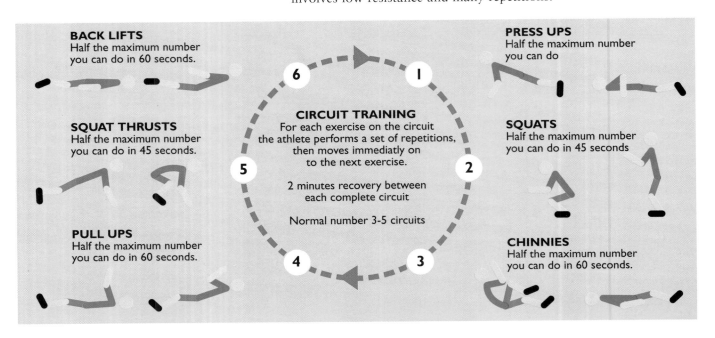

BACK LIFTS
Half the maximum number you can do in 60 seconds.

SQUAT THRUSTS
Half the maximum number you can do in 45 seconds.

PULL UPS
Half the maximum number you can do in 60 seconds.

PRESS UPS
Half the maximum number you can do

SQUATS
Half the maximum number you can do in 45 seconds

CHINNIES
Half the maximum number you can do in 60 seconds.

CIRCUIT TRAINING
For each exercise on the circuit the athlete performs a set of repetitions, then moves immediatly on to the next exercise.

2 minutes recovery between each complete circuit

Normal number 3-5 circuits

Plyometrics - Another method of developing power is by using exercises such as rebound jumping, bounding, and hopping. Such exercises that involve the contraction of muscles from a stretched position are known as plyometrics. This type of exercise can cause injuries and should only be attempted as part of an organised training programme.

Mobility and Flexibility Training

Stretching exercises can cause injury if the body is not 'warmed up' properly *(see Injury Prevention: p.106)*, and the movements are not smooth. There are three main types of these exercises *(see also p.40)*.

Passive Stretching - This is where the subject's relaxed limb is moved to a stretched position by a partner.

Active Stretching - This is where the subject moves their own limbs to a stretched position by contracting the muscles of that limb.

Ballistic Stretching - This is where the subject swings their limb*(s)* through a range of positions.

With the help of your teacher, plan, undertake, and evaluate a training programme for an activity in which you are involved in.

1 Identify one area to focus on; for example:

- continuous training;
- intermittent training;
- mobility and flexibility training;
- skill training.

2 Work out how much time per week, how many sessions per week, and how many weeks can be spent on the programme.

3 Discuss your ideas with your teacher. Organise the schedule. Remember the warm-up, warm-down, and safety etc.

4 Test yourself before you *(or those that will do your programme)* start and find the starting level.

5 Undertake the programme, and record any progress.

6 Retest at the end of the programme.

7 Consider what you did. How could you improve it next time?

Remember be realistic and practical. Take care!

Skill Training

New skills should be learned when you are fresh, not tired. This allows you to concentrate, and not be affected by fatigue or pain which will affect co-ordination and control. Once you have learned skills, you can practise them under fatigue conditions, and prepare yourself for the type of situation in which you will have to perform *(see Skill/Learning/Motivation/and Mental Preparation: pages 14-33)*.

14.6 Principles of Movement

Basic movement principles apply to all physical activities. Understanding and identifying them is an important part of observing, analysing, and improving performance. Let's look at some of them.

Skilled Movement

Physical skills need the muscles and the joints of the body to be used in specific ways. You need to know the skills in your activity, and how to observe, analyse and improve them.

For example, you might observe and analyse a badminton player performing a forehand drive through:

◆ their movement to the shuttle;
◆ their body position for the shot;
◆ the racket swing;
◆ the contact with the shuttle;
◆ the follow through;
◆ the recovery from the shot.

If any part is found faulty, the muscle/joint action can be analysed, eg. the wrist action in a flick, and improvements made. You could use a check list to identify any elements that might need improving. Then you could organise practices to improve the faulty element.

Motion and Force

Motion is about movement, that is the change of position of an object. Newton's Third Law states that when one object exerts a force on a second object, there is a force equal in magnitude *(size)*, but opposite in direction, exerted by the second on the first. This can be stated as:

"to every action, there is an equal and opposite reaction."

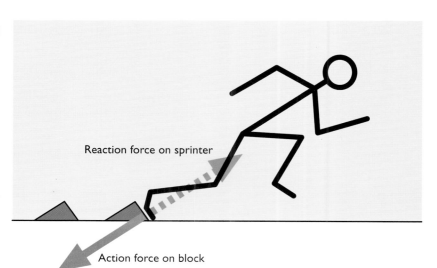

Reaction force on sprinter

Action force on block

This reaction force determines the change in speed and direction of the movement. For example, in any 'feint' or 'sidestep' you need to push down hard with your leg on the ground in the opposite direction to the one in which you want to go. Runners push backwards on the starting blocks with their legs in order to move forwards.

It is important to observe and analyse the change in direction and/or speed of any movement in terms of Newton's Third Law.

Stability

The stability of your body affects your movements. Let's have a look at how you can improve stability.

Base of Support - Your base of support involves the relationship between you and the surface you are performing on. In general, increasing the area of the base of support will make you more stable. For example, if you stand with your feet shoulder width apart, you are more stable in relation to any force applied from the side, than if your feet were close together.

Centre of Gravity - This is a point about which your weight is evenly distributed in any position. When your centre of gravity is over your base of support, you are stable. When it is outside your base of support, you are in an unstable position - a position of imbalance. If you lower your centre of gravity *(eg. by lowering your body weight by bending your knees)*, or bring your centre of gravity nearer to the middle *(centre)* of your base, you will become more stable. It is important that when you observe and analyse movements you consider the position of the centre of gravity. Sometimes you want to be in a stable position. At other times instability is needed, for example at the start of a movement. Ask your teacher to help you find the position of the centre of gravity of a movement.

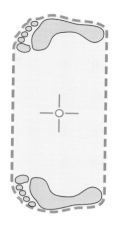

Feet shoulder width apart, broad base of support, stable position.

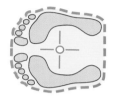

Feet close together, narrow base of support, unstable position.

In this handstand the cross represents the centre of gravity, the white lines on the mat the base of support, and the arrow the line of gravity acting on the centre of gravity.

The Player in white is in an unstable position at the start of a movement, with his centre of gravity outside of his base of support.

KEYWORDS

- P.E.
- Exercise
- Health - Related Exercise
- Children
- Training
- Planning
- Specificity
- Frequency
- Intensity
- Time *(Duration)*
- Target Heart Rate
- Aerobic
- Anaerobic
- Mobility/Flexibility
- Strength
- Cardiovascular-Respiratory Endurance
- Muscular Endurance
- Body Composition
- Progressive loading
- Reversibility
- Variation
- Continuous
- Intermittent
- Interval
- Fartlek
- Circuit
- Weight Training
- Plyometrics
- Resistance Training
- Speed Drills,
- Skill
- Movement Principles
- Observing
- Analysing
- Improving
- Motor Programme
- Joints
- Muscles
- Motion
- Force
- Newton's Law
- Stability
- Base of Support
- Centre of Gravity

Question Box ?

From what you have read, try to answer these questions.

1 What should you include in a health-promoting exercise programme?

2 What do frequency, intensity, time, and type *(F.I.T.T.)* mean?

3 What is circuit training?

4 What, in simple language, does Newton's Third Law mean?

CHECK LIST

✔ Health–Related Exercise is important in National Curriculum P.E.

✔ Individuals exercise for different reasons.

✔ Children differ from adults anatomically, and physiologically, & therefore adapt to exercise differently.

✔ Training should take into account frequency, duration, & intensity.

✔ The principles of training include planning, specificity, progressive loading, reversibility, & variation.

✔ The types of training are continuous, intermittent, mobility/flexibility, and skill.

✔ Understanding & identifying the principles of movement is an important part of observing, analysing, & improving performance.

✔ Physical skills need the muscles & joints of the body to be used in specific ways. These can be observed, analysed, & improved.

✔ To every action there is an equal & opposite reaction.

✔ Stability is affected by your base of support & your centre of gravity.

15 SAFETY IN P.E.

Physical activities, because of their physical nature, involve physical risks. The Health and Safety at Work Act, 1974, describes the responsibilities of employers to people who work for them *(employees)*. Within these responsibilities, there is a duty to ensure that:

"...persons not in...employment who may be affected are not exposed to risks to their health or safety."

In other words even as a pupil at school, although you are not actually employed by the school, the school has a responsibility not to expose you to any unacceptable risks to your health or safety.

This applies to you in your P.E. lessons.

There are various safety codes in existence for P.E., based mostly on good practice. Teachers have to be aware of dangers and risks, and take steps to deal with them. This idea is part of the 'parental' responsibility role that teachers have. Schools and teachers have to make sure that:

◆ surfaces, equipment and buildings are safe;
◆ that procedures for safety, first aid and emergencies are in place;
◆ pupils are warned of the risks and discouraged from inappropriate behaviour;
◆ pupils are prepared properly for the activity;
◆ the activity follows approved and appropriate guidelines and that they take all necessary safety measures;
◆ parental consent is obtained for trips, outdoor and adventurous activities etc.

Teachers need to know about anything that might affect pupils taking part in physical activities, including personal fears, asthma, disabilities, diabetes, heart problems, epilepsy etc., and they need to treat that information confidentially, and with understanding of the potential embarrassment for the person involved.

First Aid boxes should be available, properly equipped with contents, which should include a guidance card, sterile dressings of various sizes, individual wrapped adhesive dressings, eye pads, triangular bandages, safety pins, sterile water, disposable gloves, and blunt nosed scissors. *(Many schools are not allowed to keep plasters due to the possibility of allergic reaction)*. Teachers are also encouraged to know first aid procedures, and to have a recognised first aid qualification.

Safety requirements for specific activities are available from National Governing Bodies and Associations. Some activities, including outdoor pursuits and swimming, require a specific qualification to be held by the teacher, in addition to a recognised teaching certificate or degree.

Action Box

1 Describe the safety measures that your teacher takes in an activity in which you participate.

2 Write down all the things you could do to help make things as safe as possible.

3 List things that could be done to make things safer.

4 Describe how behaviour is involved in safe practice.

With your teacher's permission discuss these ideas in class.

Unsafe lifting technique

Have you considered what you should do to make a situation as safe as possible?

Think about how pupils behave and what they know about safety in P.E.

- Could you behave in a safer way (*eg. not chewing while performing, not messing about etc.*)?
- What should you do with personal items of jewellry, watches etc.?
- Do you know the correct ways of supporting people in some activities?
- Do you know how to handle, get out, put away equipment safely?
- Do you get carried away sometimes, and lose your self control?
- Do you wear the correct clothes and safety equipment for the activity (*eg. shin guards, hand guards, gum shields etc.*)?
- Do you know where the First Aid boxes are?
- Are you properly prepared to take part in the activity? Do you know what to do, and how to do it?
- Do you follow your teacher's instructions?
- Do you warm-up and warm-down (*cool-down*) properly?

There are many things that you can do to make P.E. safe and fun. You do rely on others to guide you, and make sure things are safe for you, but there's a lot that you can do. Being safe in P.E. involves you in partnership with your teachers and other pupils.

Safe Lifting

You can injure yourself if you don't lift properly. Back pain can be bad, and affect health and participation in physical activities, therefore:

- make sure that you only lift weights/objects that you can manage;
- bend your knees, keep your back straight, and use the leg, hip, and shoulder muscles, they are normally stronger than your arms;
- the weight should be as close as possible to the body;
- your feet should be about shoulder width apart.

These principles apply whether you are lifting by yourself or with others. Always be careful!

Safe lifting technique

CHECK LIST

✔ *Pupils should not be exposed to health & safety risks.*

✔ *Schools & teachers have a duty of care.*

✔ *Specific safety guidelines are available for all activities.*

✔ *You can help make P.E. safe.*

✔ *Safe lifting is important.*

KEYWORDS

- Health and Safety
- Behaviour
- Safe Lifting
- First Aid.

16 INJURY

Have you ever injured yourself in P.E.? If you have, what sort of injuries have you had? Have you performed again too quickly after injury, and hurt yourself in the same way again? I expect most of us have been frustrated by injuries just when we least wanted them. That happens to top class performers as well.

Most injuries are relatively minor and, if treated properly, get better quickly, and don't occur again. Some injuries are more serious, and keep happening. It is often our own fault for not taking care, not looking after the injury properly when it has happened, and exercising again too soon after the injury. We're all impatient to get going again. In the long run, this often makes matters worse.

Sometimes of course, even when all precautions and great care have been taken, accidents can still happen. However, the risk of accidents will be reduced if the commonest causes of accidents are understood, and all precautions are taken.

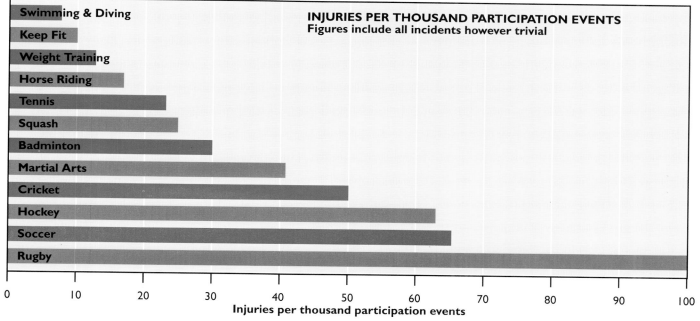

INJURIES PER THOUSAND PARTICIPATION EVENTS
Figures include all incidents however trivial

Swimming & Diving
Keep Fit
Weight Training
Horse Riding
Tennis
Squash
Badminton
Martial Arts
Cricket
Hockey
Soccer
Rugby

0   10   20   30   40   50   60   70   80   90   100

Injuries per thousand participation events

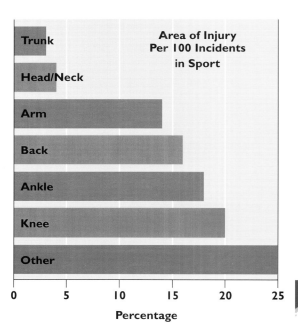

Area of Injury Per 100 Incidents in Sport

(Bar chart showing Percentage on x-axis from 0 to 25)

- Trunk
- Head/Neck
- Arm
- Back
- Ankle
- Knee
- Other

Percentage

16.1 Prevention

What could you do to prevent injuries happening? Sometimes there's not much that you can do. It helps if training is progressive and safe, with proper rest periods. Proper conditioning of the body, and the right mental attitude are important in reducing the risk of injury.

Correct Warm-up and Warm-down

Impatience often makes us ignore the need for a good warm-up before we start, and a gentle warm-down after we've finished. A warm-up prepares the mind and the body for the activity, and helps reduce the risk of injury. It should involve a gradual increase in the heart rate and breathing rate. Stretching exercises are also important. By the end of a warm-up session you should have focussed your mind, and feel physically ready to begin.

A warm down reverses the warm-up process, and brings the mind and the body back to a more relaxed state. It helps to begin to repay the oxygen debt by maintaining an increased blood flow to the muscles which delivers oxygen to the tissues, and helps remove the lactic acid. Stretching exercises after work outs can also help to relax the body.

Correct equipment

Make sure that you use the correct equipment for the activity and wear the right clothing. Protect the ankles, knees, hips, and back by wearing the correct footwear. Clothing should also be comfortable. Equipment should be approved and safe. Be aware of safe practice, and safety rules. Activities should always be properly supervised, with First Aid equipment and materials available. The surface you are performing on should always be safe, and in appropriate condition.

Correct preparation

Always prepare yourself properly for the activity. You should develop the right skills, strategies, frame of mind, and body condition to perform well. Understand the rules. Not knowing what to do causes mistakes and injuries.

Enough rest and recovery

Never come back too soon after an injury. Seek advice and, if necessary, proper treatment when injured. Don't be pressurised into performing before you know you're ready. Don't feel guilty about taking time to recovery properly.

16.2 Causes

Parts of the body can be injured either through sudden impact or movement, or through over use. If such injuries keep occurring, more lasting damage can occur. Injuries can also occur because of environmental factors such as equipment, and the surface etc. *(see Equipment and surfaces: p.52).*

16.3 Types of Injuries

There are many different injuries that might occur. Let's examine a few of them that you might experience.

Winding

If you are winded by being struck in the stomach, you'll find it difficult to breathe and speak. You might feel a little sick, and the top part of your stomach will hurt. You need to lean forward and massage the stomach. Gradually the effect will wear off.

Nose bleeds

If you have a nose bleed don't tilt your head back. Sit down and bend your head forward a little, breathe through your mouth, pinch the soft part of your nose for about 10 minutes, or until the bleeding stops. Always loosen any tight clothing around your neck, and don't blow your nose for several hours or you will start the bleeding again. If you keep having the problem then see your doctor.

Blisters

These are caused by friction on the skin. The blister protects the injured area. Normally you cover them up to stop further damage.

Cuts and Grazes

These happen all the time. Always make sure there is no dirt in the cut or graze, and clean it with fresh water. If there is bleeding, place a clean dressing *(pad of gauze or cloth)* on the cut or graze, and gently apply pressure to stop the bleeding. A sticky plaster can be used to hold the dressing in place. Get help if the cut is severe. If the blood is spurting out this means that an artery has been cut, which is very serious. In this case apply as much pressure to the dressing over the wound as you can, if possible raise the injured part above the level of the heart and send for help straight away.

The 'heel-tab' on some shoes can cause blisters and inflame the 'Achilles' tendon *(see p.52).*

Especial care must be taken with cuts in contact sports.

Bruises

We often get bruised. Severe bruising could indicate a broken or fractured bone. Bruising is a sign of internal bleeding. For a normal bruise, raise the injured part, and apply an ice pack.

Muscle Injuries

Always seek advice with these injuries. When you injure muscle fibres it is called a strain, a pull, or a tear, depending upon the amount of damage done. A torn muscle involves many muscle fibres being damaged, with much internal bleeding within the muscle. It is this bleeding that causes the swelling. Always support and rest muscle injuries. You can use rest, ice, compression and elevation to treat them.

Tendon and Ligament Injuries

Tendons join muscles to bones, often around a joint. They can become inflamed *(tendonitis)*, or ruptured as can happen to the Achilles tendon at the heel.

Ligaments join bones together at joints. They can be sprained or torn when a joint is twisted through a range of movement that is not normal. Always support and rest them. You can use rest, ice, compression and elevation to treat them.

Bones and Joints

These can be broken or dislocated. Get help immediately. First aid treatment is needed involving support, use of splints, and treatment for shock. Medical help is required.

Loss of Consciousness

Although not strictly an injury, loss of consciousness can be associated with injury, eg. a blow to the head. Loss of consciousness can also be associated with near drowning.

16.4 What can You do for Yourself?

Ice pack

If you experience pain from an injury, don't try to carry on, or you could make it worse. You should stop, rest the injured part, and seek help. For some injuries *(bruises, swellings etc)* rest, ice, compression and elevation can help to reduce the pain and limit the injury.

Rest + **I**ce + **C**ompression + **E**levation = **R.I.C.E.**

Put an ice-pack or cold compress on the injured part as quickly as possible *(a bag of frozen peas could be used)*. This helps slow down the blood flow to the injured part, and reduces internal bleeding.

Bandaging the injured area firmly helps reduce the swelling, this is called compression. Don't make the bandage too tight.

Try to raise the injured part. This will reduce the blood flow and the pressure of fluid on the injured area. This is called elevation.

Don't just leave the injury. Apply these simple self-help methods, and get advice. Proper treatment can help to strengthen the injured part as it heals.

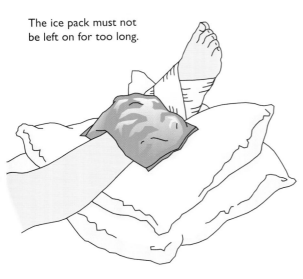

The ice pack must not be left on for too long.

16.5 Principles of First Aid & Life Saving

Knowing what to do when help is needed is important. First Aid courses *(eg. Red Cross/ St John Ambulance/ St Andrew's Ambulance)*, and Life Saving courses *(eg. Royal Life Saving Association)* are available. Why not take one of these courses and learn properly!

Let's examine a few of the basic principles.

First Aid is the treatment given by the first person to arrive at the scene. It is better if the First Aider is properly trained, regularly re-assessed, and has current knowledge and skills. A first aider should:

◆ think about the situation;
◆ make a decision about what is wrong;
◆ act quickly and correctly;
◆ hand on to more qualified people as soon as possible.

First aiders should not expose themselves to danger when helping the casualty, and should try to prevent any further danger if possible. The most seriously injured ones should be treated first. The First Aider should always check that the injured person can breathe, and try to stop any bleeding. If they are conscious only move them if they are in danger. The casualty should be covered and made as comfortable as possible, and if conscious talked to in a calm reassuring way. In this way, a First Aider will help to preserve life, and aid recovery.

In an initial assessment of the casualty these principles are sometimes stated as **D.R.A.B.C.**

Danger -
    is there any danger to First Aider*(s)* and injured person*(s)*?
Response -
    what is the response of injured person, eg. unconscious etc.?
Airway -
    is it blocked?
Breathing -
    is the person breathing?
Circulation -
    is the pulse OK?

Life saving involves the same principles, but has special considerations of its own.

Keeping the airways open

The First Aider should try to keep the airways open so that the person can breathe. To do this, first check that a caualty's airway is not blocked by their tongue, false teeth, etc. Then tilt the head gently by pulling the jaw up, using the first two fingers of one hand, while at the same time pressing the forehead backwards with the 'heel' of the other hand.

If a conscious person is choking on something, firm blows to the person's back can dislodge the blockage.

If the person is unconscious but is breathing and has a pulse, and no other life threatening conditions, they should always be placed in the recovery position. Some injuries may affect how you turn and support an unconscious casualty in the recovery position. The recovery position prevents the tongue blocking the airways, and the swallowing of any blood and saliva.

St. John Ambulance

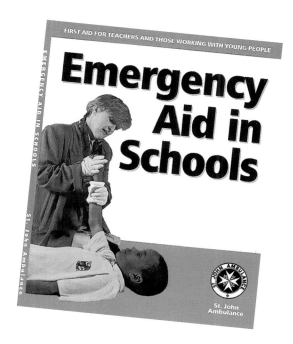

FIRST AID FOR TEACHERS AND THOSE WORKING WITH YOUNG PEOPLE

EMERGENCY AID IN SCHOOLS

Emergency Aid in Schools

St John Ambulance

St. John Ambulance

The recovery position

◆ The First Aider kneels beside the casualty who is flat on their back;

◆ if the casualty is wearing glasses they are removed;

◆ the arm nearest the First Aider is placed at right angles to the person's body, with the elbow bent and the palm facing up;

◆ the arm furthest from the First Aider is placed across the chest with the palm of the hand resting against the nearest cheek;

◆ the casualty's furthest thigh is pulled up raising the knee up, with the foot of that leg flat on the ground;

◆ the thigh is pulled and the casualty is rolled towards the First Aider onto their side, with their hand still pressed to the cheek;

◆ the upper leg, hip and knee are bent at right angles;

◆ lift chin forward into the open airway position, adjust hand under the cheek as necessary

◆ check casualty cannot roll forwards or backwards;

◆ check breathing and pulse frequently, if they stop take the appropriate action.

When the casualty has been placed into this position, an ambulance is sent for, and anything that happens *(state of consciousness etc.)* is noted. The casualty should not be given anything to eat or drink.

The pulse is best taken at the neck using two fingers, not the thumb. With the head tilted back, feel for the Adam's apple. Slide your fingers back towards you into the gap between the Adam's apple and the strap muscle *(see p.63)*, and feel for the pulse in the neck. Feel for at least 5 seconds before deciding the pulse is absent.

Accidents occur in water as well as land. Life saving is part of a P.E. programme. Once the person has been recovered from the water, they can be placed in the recovery position.

The First Aider must be patient and careful. Shock is lessened by comforting words.

First Aid and Life Saving courses will teach you how to do heart/breathing *(cardio/pulmonary)* resuscitation *(reviving)* by chest compression, and mouth to mouth or artificial ventilation.

Question Box ?

From what you have read, try to answer these questions.

1 What could you do to prevent injuries occurring?

2 How can rest, ice, compression, and elevation help certain injuries?

3 What is 'winding' and how can you treat it?

4 What are bruises, and how can you treat them?

5 Describe a safe lifting technique.

Basics of cardio/pulmonary resuscitation *(CPR)*

If the casualty is unconscious, not breathing, and has no pulse:

◆ dial 999 for an ambulance;
◆ quickly reassess the DRABC, if the casualty is still unconscious, not breathing, and has no pulse, apply mouth to mouth ventilations together with chest compressions *(CPR)* until help arrives.

Mouth to mouth ventilation involves the following steps:

◆ open the airway by tilting their head back;
◆ pinch their nose firmly closed;
◆ take a deep breath and seal your lips around the casualty's mouth;
◆ blow into their mouth until their chest rises;
◆ remove your mouth, turn your head away to breathe in, and allow their chest to fall;
◆ continue at a rate of 10 breaths a minute *(for a child 20 breaths per minute)*;
◆ check for a pulse after every 10 breaths *(for a child every 20 breaths)*;
◆ if the pulse is absent commence chest compressions together with mouth to mouth ventilation *(CPR)*;
◆ if breathing starts, place them in the recovery position.

Chest compression is a rhythmic compression of the chest, which keeps the blood moving round the body, and in a small number of cases can restart the heart. The technique varies with the age of the person being treated *(infant, child, or adult)* due to the different strength of the chest. The technique described here is for adults.

Chest compressions together with mouth to mouth ventilation *(CPR)* involves the following: *(note that chest compressions must always be combined with mouth to mouth ventilation)*

◆ give two breaths of mouth to mouth ventilation;
◆ place heel of hand two finger breadths above the junction of the rib margin and breastbone;
◆ place other hand on top and interlock fingers, keeping your arms straight and your fingers off the chest, press down about 4-5 cms *(1.5-2 inches)*, release pressure, keeping your hands in place;
◆ repeat the compressions 15 times, aiming at a rate of 80 per minute;
◆ continue resuscitation, 2 breaths to 15 compressions;
◆ only if the casualty's colour improves, check the pulse;
◆ if the pulse is present, stop the chest compressions but continue to ventilate if necessary.

These methods need learning and practising under expert tuition.
WHY NOT ENROL ON A FIRST AID COURSE!

Plastic models can be used to demonstrate the principles of mouth to mouth resuscitation and chest compression technique, and to practice on safely.

CHECK LIST

✔ You can help to prevent injuries.

✔ Injuries do occur in physical activities.

✔ There are many different injuries including winding, cuts & grazes, bruises, muscle, tendon and ligament injuries, & injuries to bones and joints.

✔ Rest, Ice, Compression, & Elevation (RICE) can be used to treat some injuries eg sprained joints.

✔ First aiders should be qualified.

✔ The recovery position prevents the tongue from blocking the airways, & the swallowing of any blood & saliva.

KEYWORDS

● Injuries
● Prevention
● Causes
● Winding
● Nose bleeds
● Cuts and Grazes
● Bruises
● Muscle
● Tendon
● Ligament
● Bones
● Joints
● Rest, Ice, Compression Elevation
● Lifting Principles
● Airway
● Recovery position
● First Aid

Examination Box Two

a) In your P.E. lessons, what should you do with jewellery and watches?

(1 Mark)

b) Identify two pieces of safety equipment used in any physical activity.

(2 Marks)

c) When treating injuries, what does R.I.C.E. mean?   *(3 Marks)*

d) What is involved in:

◆ losing weight   *(2 Marks)*

◆ gaining weight   *(2 Marks)*

◆ 'making the weight' ?   *(2 Marks)*

e)

i) Identify four of the principles of training.   *(4 Marks)*

The table charts a weight training programme using the bench press exercise with a 50 kilo weight, over six sessions.

Session	No. of reps	Size of weight
1	5	50 kilo
2	10	50 kilo
3	13	50 kilo
4	15	50 kilo
5	15	50 kilo
6	15	50 kilo

ii) Give the total number of kilos lifted in session 6   *(1 Mark)*

iii) Explain why the number of repetitions in session 2 showed a significant increase over the number of repetitions in session 1.

(2 Marks)

iv) Which of the principles of training are being used when the repetitions are increased in this way?

(1 Mark)

(Total Marks = 20)

Reasons, Opportunities & Issues Affecting Participation in Physical Activity

OBJECTIVES

To enable the reader to understand the following reasons, opportunities, and issues affecting participation.

◆ Leisure and Physical Recreation.
◆ Local provision.
◆ Qualifications and Employment.
◆ National Organisations affecting participation.
◆ Participation, excellence, and the Olympic ideal.
◆ Issues affecting participation.

With the help of your teacher, discuss which of the following could be considered as taking place in what you would think of as leisure time.

1 Your P.E. lessons.

2 Voluntary lunchtime and after school activities.

3 Playing for your School/County etc.

4 Belonging to a club.

5 Taking part in a physical activity at a leisure centre in the evening.

6 Playing at your local park with your friends.

17 LEISURE & PHYSICAL RECREATION

There are opportunities for taking part in physical activities at school, clubs, and leisure centres etc. Some of these opportunities are part of your P.E. programme. Many of them are in your leisure time. The time you have for leisure activities is important. Before we look at the reasons you might have for taking part, and the factors that might affect you taking part, have a go at this action box!

17.1 Leisure

There is more leisure time now for most people in this country than there was in the 19th or early part of the 20th Century. People live longer now than they used to, they can retire earlier, in general the working week has got shorter, and many have holidays with pay.

However, whether or not leisure time will continue to expand in the future is less certain than it used to be. An increasing number of people have part-time jobs or are unemployed, and these people may well not consider this as an increase in their leisure time.

There are many different ways of describing leisure. The most common way is to contrast leisure with work, and time spent eating *(not eating out socially)*, and sleeping. Leisure time can be spent in many different ways. We watch TV, read books, go to the cinema, play or listen to music, and daydream in our leisure time. Sometimes we take part in physical activities. Some of these activities may have been learned at school in P.E., or in clubs and groups to which we belong. In this way, participation and performance in physical activities have become part of our use of leisure time.

17.2 Physical Recreation

Recreation is the process or means of entertaining oneself or relaxing in leisure time. If this is achieved through physical activity, then it is referred to as physical recreation.

Physical Recreation provides opportunities for people to meet each other, to develop shared interests, to take part in exercise, to have fun, and to relax. This helps reduce the stress that can affect people. Many of the Sports Council's campaigns *(see Sports Council: p.126)* have tried to promote the link between taking part in physical activities and the use of leisure time.

17.3 Community Physical Recreation

Community physical recreation is an attempt to provide individuals and groups, with access to, and opportunities to take part in, a range of physical recreational activities at a local level. The increase in community groups, community centres, and community facilities in general, increasingly makes this possible.

The idea of community brings a more 'human' feeling to such provision. But there are problems with this type of provision. For example there can be disputes between the community members, or professional workers and officers, about who is to decide what such a programme will consist of, or the distribution of funding.

Opportunities for the Disadvantaged

Opportunities to participate vary from area to area, typically as a result of differences in funding. As resources are limited, there have been efforts to target groups in society who are disadvantaged with regard to opportunities for participation. Groups disadvantaged in this way have been helped to participate through subsidies of various types, including reduced or free membership schemes, grants and help with transport etc.

Such opportunities have been targeted at women in general and mothers with young children in particular, ethnic minorities, the disabled, the unemployed, the elderly, and young people. These programmes have included 'taster' courses, day events, play schemes, and specific facility provision *(kick-about areas etc)*. As even less money becomes available, there is pressure to cut back on this type of provision.

Action Box

1 Describe what extra leisure facilities you would like to see provided in your area.

2 Describe what extra activity programmes you would like to see provided in your area.

Question Box ?

From what you have read, try to answer these questions.

1. What is leisure?

2. What does the phrase, 'physical recreation' mean?

3. How have disadvantaged groups been helped to participate in physical recreation?

CHECK LIST

✔ Leisure is often contrasted with work and time spent eating (not eating out socially) & sleeping.

✔ Participation and performance in physical activities can occur in leisure time.

✔ Physical recreation could refer to a programme of physical activities which occur in leisure time.

✔ Physical recreation is the process or means of entertaining oneself or relaxing by physical activity in leisure time.

✔ Community physical recreation is an attempt to provide individuals and groups with access to & opportunities in a range of physical recreational activities.

✔ As resources are limited, there have been efforts to target disadvantaged groups in society.

KEYWORDS

● Leisure
● Physical Activity
● Performance
● Participation
● Physical Recreation
● Community Physical Recreation
● Targeting
● Disadvantaged Groups
● Access
● Opportunities
● Resources

Action Box

1 List the physical activities that you take part in.

2 Identify the main reasons you have for taking part in them.

3 Put the reasons in order of importance (*prioritise the list*).

4 Compare your list with your friends, and with the permission of your teacher discuss what you have found.

Action Box

Try to put each of the reasons listed in the text for taking part, into one of the following six categories

1 Enjoyment.

2 To learn skills.

3 Fitness and health reasons.

4 Social involvement.

5 Use of leisure time.

6 For rewards of some kind.

18 PARTICIPATION

Why is it that many people participate *(take part)* in one type of physical activity or another, and others do not? There are many reasons, and they often depend on the nature of the activity, or the situation involved.

Before we try to list a few reasons, have a go at the action boxes!

Reasons for Taking Part

Now let's list some reasons why people do take part. Which of these would motivate you? Can you think of any others?

◆ For enjoyment and fun.
◆ To get fit/stay fit/get fitter.
◆ To compete and try to win.
◆ To show that you are good at something.
◆ To express something that you feel.
◆ To meet others.
◆ To do something worthwhile.
◆ Your friends do it.
◆ You like a challenge.
◆ It is new and different.
◆ For excitement and thrills.
◆ You find it satisfying.
◆ To play in a team.
◆ To perform alone.
◆ For interest.
◆ To perform at representative level *(county etc.)*.
◆ To participate in some way.
◆ Someone makes you.
◆ To please others.
◆ You feel you ought to.

There are many other reasons. How did yours compare?

Reasons for Not Taking Part

Now let's list some reasons why people do not take part. Is there anything on the list that stops you from taking part in an activity that you would otherwise like to do?

◆ Lack of time.
◆ Lack of money.
◆ Lack of interest.
◆ Your friends don't do it.
◆ It scares you.
◆ Lack of confidence.
◆ Lack of ability.
◆ Lack of access.
◆ Lack of transport.
◆ Apathy *(can't be bothered).*
◆ Disability, or some other medical reason.

Whatever the reason, should you bother? There are so many things that you could do, why not take the opportunity while you can? It may never come again. Ask your teachers, parents and friends, and go for it!

Factors Affecting Participation

There are many factors that might affect your participation in physical activities. Some of them are personal, some social, and some involve the opportunities available to you. Let's look at some of them in more detail.

Personal Factors

These include personality, age, gender, ethnic background, motivation, interest, attitudes, skills, and confidence.

Social Factors

These include your occupation, how much money you have/earn, transport, friends, education, and background.

Opportunities

Opportunities available to you not only involve access to facilities, where the facilities are located, the choice available, how they are advertised etc., but also your awareness of those opportunities.

Many of these are interrelated, affect each other, and involve your reasons for participation.

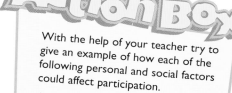

Question Box ?

From what you have read, try to answer these questions.

1 Why do people participate in physical activity? Give four reasons.

2 Why do some people not participate in physical activity?
Give four reasons.

Action Box

With the help of your teacher try to give an example of how each of the following personal and social factors could affect participation.

Age   Gender
Interest   Motivation.
Skills   Background.
Education   Money
Transport   Friends
Confidence

The map below shows a town & its facilities for physical activities. Which side of the river would you prefer to live? Make a plan of your area and mark in all the amenities and transport links you can.
How could it be improved?
Which facilities do you use, or would like to use, regularly?

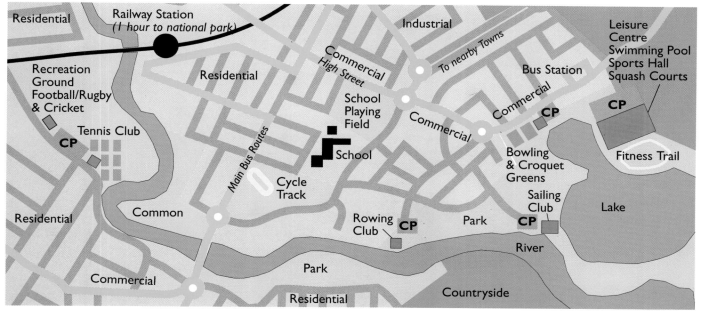

KEYWORDS

- Participation
- Reasons
- Personal Factors
- Social Factors
- Opportunities
- Interests
- Women
- School
- Culture
- Children Act

CHECK LIST

✔ There are many reasons why people take part in physical recreation including enjoyment, exercise, and competition.

✔ There are many reasons why people don't bother to take part in physical recreation, including lack of time, lack of opportunity, & boredom.

Our interests can change as we get older, especially if we earn more money. We might become more aware of opportunities that we didn't notice before, and acquire the confidence and money to try them.

Many women are now challenging the traditional view that they should only take part in certain types of activity (see *Women in Sport: p.143*).

Your cultural background, that is the community that you come from and its traditions, can influence the type of activities you get involved in.

Experiences at school can affect you. **National Curriculum P.E.** emphasises the importance of developing an understanding of health-promoting exercise, and of experiencing a wide choice of different activities. In **Key Stage 4** *(14-16 years)*, at least one game has to be chosen, reflecting the traditional importance of games, and particularly team games, in this country.

In general, the highest participation rates in physical recreation are still found amongst those with professions *(doctors, teachers, solicitors, office staff etc)* rather than other groups such as unskilled workers. Reasons for this would include education, interests, awareness of opportunities, and income. Access to facilities involves cost and travel. The location of a sports centre or park etc. is important, especially when there are transport problems.

Participation is related to all these factors and more. People have to make choices about what to do, and when to do it. If an activity is really important to you, you'll find a way to do it, regardless of the obstacles in your way.

The Children Act

The 1991 Children Act is aimed mainly at local authorities.
The Act requires local authorities to;

◆ Hold a register of all activities for children under the age of eight that are supervised, held on their premises, last over two hours and run more than six times a year.

◆ Provide activities and services that ensure the health and development of all children in need.

These duties must be reviewed every three years. The register includes sport activities run by the local authority and by voluntary organisations. The quality of the activities has to be measured. Both the premises and the organisation has to be registered.

The act emphasises the importance of the needs of a child. Coaches and teachers must be suitably qualified, provide safe activities, and give sufficient information to parents about the activity. Some authorities may require coaches to undergo a police check to show that no record of offenses affecting behaviour with children exists. Most governing bodies now issue guidelines on these matters.

19 LOCAL PROVISION

Local provision for physical activities involves a combination of the public and private sectors, and voluntary organisations.

Opportunities to participate in physical recreation activities at a local level include the use of leisure centres, swimming pools, playing fields, golf courses, playgrounds, all-weather kick-about areas, country parks, footpaths, theatres, community arts centres, community centres, youth clubs, and halls.

Local Authorities provide a service to the public within set financial limits. Local Authorities usually operate in partnership with commercial and voluntary organisations. They also work with regional Sports Councils and Arts Councils.

Voluntary and local groups involve a large number of people. They work with Local Authorities, regional Sports and Arts Councils, and private organisations for the benefit of their members and the community as a whole. They do not normally set out to make a profit. If any profit is made it is normally put back into the group's finances.

A local Sports Centre built next to, and shared by a school..

Compulsory Competitive Tendering *(CCT)*

This was introduced as part of the 1988 Local Government Act, in an attempt to reduce the cost of operating such facilities. CCT allows various groups to bid for contracts to supply various services. CCT had to begin by 1992/3.

The contracts usually last for 4–6 years, and are normally based on the successful bidder operating a service across all the local authority recreational provision. The private sector can compete for contracts on a cost effective basis. The local authority retains ownership of the facility whilst the private company manages it on a day to day basis.

Local authorities have established 'direct labour and services organisations' so that they can also compete for tenders. Local authorities have had to restructure to accomplish this, and have had to separate the 'client' side from the 'contractors' side, within the organisation.

For the private sector, CCT has provided new business opportunities. As profit becomes increasingly important, some fear that the idea of 'public services' will be lost, and that community groups and disadvantaged groups will suffer. Others believe it is an essential step towards modernising this type of provision, and reducing costs.

The private sector provides facilities, and opportunities with a view to making a profit. In general this type of provision would cater for popular activities and social opportunities which would attract the most customers, and therefore generate the most income.

Areas of provision involved in CCT have included catering, equipment hire, supervisory staffing, marketing and publicity, maintenance services and security.

'Value for Money'

CCT has emphasised 'value for money', which involves the evaluation of both the quality and the quantity of the service provided. It has required improved cost effectiveness which has often included cost cutting measures, staff flexibility, and improved strategic planning within the Local Authority organisation.

Examine your local area on a map and identify opportunities for participation in physical recreation activities within:

1 a 2 mile radius; and

2 from 2 to 10 miles radius.

Compare these with other facilities in your region, and with the permission of your teacher discuss your findings in class.

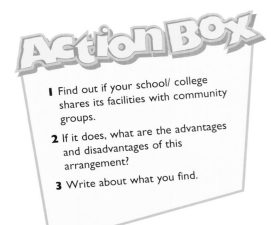

Action Box

1 Find out if your school/ college shares its facilities with community groups.

2 If it does, what are the advantages and disadvantages of this arrangement?

3 Write about what you find.

Adults can use school and college facilities in the evenings.

Dual Use & Joint Provision

A government leaflet in 1964, identified the need to share school and other educational facilities with users who were not students, or staff. This idea was called 'dual use'. New facilities could also be developed to provide jointly for the needs of different groups eg. students and clubs, thereby reducing costs. This was called 'joint provision'.

'Sport in the Community - the next 10 years' *(see p.128)* set out a target of 800 additional sports halls to be provided by 1987. The Sports Council, and the then Minister for Sport both emphasised the need for facilities operated by various agencies, eg. schools, private companies, and the Civil Service *(which owned a number of sports grounds and clubs through the Civil Service Sports Council)*, to be opened up for community use.

Both economic and social benefits were possible from such cooperation. Economic benefits included the sharing of costs between agencies, and the possibility of an increase in income. Social benefits centred on the closer ties between the community and other organisations that this cooperation would bring.

Success Stories

Schools were particularly identified as places which could benefit greatly from such cooperation. Dual use was seen as a way of quickly increasing the amount of available facilities, and of bringing schools more fully into the local community, which might then support them more. Developments in the Sidney Stringer School and Community College in Coventry, the Simon Langton School in Canterbury, the Sutton Centre in Nottinghamshire, the Village College system in Cambridgeshire, and the Community College system in Leicestershire, are all examples of the benefits of such cooperation.

The Sports Council was prepared to grant aid such schemes, working through its regional officers. Dual use and joint provision are a generally accepted part of facility development today. Regardless of the difficulties encountered along the way, they have provided communities with opportunities not previously available. Joint provision has also been attempted between local authorities and industry, but there has been relatively little progress in this area.

National Lottery Money

The government paper, 'Raising the Game' *(1995)*, emphasises the use of National Lottery money as a means of improving existing facilities, building new facilities, and buying equipment *(see Sponsorship: p.146)*. The following are quoted as successful examples of this:

◆ the Arthur Terry School, Sutton Coldfield *(£752 600 towards costs of £1 426 000 for a new fitness centre, cricket nets, etc.)*;

◆ the Cavendish School, Hemel Hempstead *(£75 000 towards overall costs of £305 252)*;

◆ the Mallory School, Bromley *(£725 500 towards overall costs of £1 117 500)*.

◆ the Mountbatten School, Romsey, Hampshire *(£380 000 for extension of Performance Arts block)*;

Dance in the new
Performance Arts block
at the Mountbatten
School, Romsey,
Hampshire.

Question Box ?

From what you have read, try to answer these questions.

1 What is Compulsory Competitive
Tendering?

2 What are **dual use** and **joint provision**?

3 What different types of facilities are
available for you to use locally? Give four
examples.

KEYWORDS

- Community
- Local Authorities
- Public, Private
- Voluntary
- Opportunities
- Facilities
- Dual Use
- Joint Provision
- Sports Council
- Local Provision
- Partnership
- National Lottery.

CHECK LIST

✔ Local opportunities for participation
involve a combination of public, private &
voluntary organisations.

✔ Compulsory Competitive Tendering was introduced
as part of the 1988 Local Government Act.

✔ Dual use and joint provision involve
sharing provision, and the joint development
of new facilities.

✔ National Lottery money can be used to
improve existing facilities, build new facilities, &
purchase equipment.

20 QUALIFICATIONS & EMPLOYMENT

Many people who enjoy physical recreation activities would like to work in an area connected with their interests. In many cases you would need a special qualification.

20.1 What Qualifications can You Get?

It is possible to study leisure, tourism, physical education, sport, dance, and health and fitness etc. in many courses at different levels. These could include the following.

◆ Various coaching, leadership, officiating and safety awards from National Governing Bodies and Associations;
◆ GCSE's, GCE AS and A levels;
◆ Foundation, Intermediate, and Advanced GNVQ *(General National Vocational Qualifications)* and NVQs or equivalent, eg. BTEC First and National Diplomas or Certificates *(EDEXCEL)*;
◆ Degrees and Higher National Diplomas/Certificates;
◆ Industry linked Certificates and Diplomas.

20.2 What Employment can You Get?

Your qualifications and level of experience would normally determine the employment opportunities available to you. Let's identify a few. Your teachers, tutors, and careers officers will help you find out more about these and other areas of opportunity.

Leisure Industry - A broad area of work based on the Leisure Industry provides many opportunities, including leisure centre attendants, supervisors, and managers; coaches, leaders, and instructors in various activities; wardens at Outdoor Pursuit Centres; personal trainers in health and fitness; ground staff, technicians; theatre personnel; and general organisers and administrators.

The Tourist Industry - Provides opportunities which include travel staff and representatives, instructors, coaches, organisers, ground staff, and attendants.

Commerce and Business - There is a great deal of overlap with the Leisure and Tourist Industries in this area. Opportunities include retail work *(clothing and equipment for dance, sport, outdoor pursuits, fitness)*; company reps; and manufacturing.

Activity Development - Opportunities exist with national, regional, and local organisations, such as the Sports Council, the Arts Councils, the Countryside Commission, individual sport Associations eg. All England Netball Association; and local Authorities. Personnel include development officers, organisers, coaches, and leaders.

The Media - A range of opportunities connected with television, radio, newspapers and magazines exist - including journalists, reporters, broadcasters, photographers, and technicians.

If you are interested in a career connected with physical activity.

1 Arrange an interview with your school careers officer.

2 Visit your 'careers room' and start to find out what you would need to do.

Physiotherapy - Opportunities exist involving injury rehabilitation and prevention, including physiotherapy, sports massage, and occupational therapy.

Education - There are opportunities for P.E. teachers, lecturers, coaches, ground staff, and technicians.

Services - There are openings for Physical Training Instructors in the Armed Forces, and Fire Service .

Professional - Many sports provide opportunities for professional and semi-professional performers in different activities. Many participants go on to other careers after they have retired from performing, often based on their reputation and experience.

Let us look at a few opportunities in more detail.

P.E. Teachers

In England and Wales P.E. teachers normally work in Secondary Schools. They have been trained to teach P.E. and often another subject, to pupils of all ability levels and all secondary age groups. Teachers in Primary Schools are trained to teach all areas of the curriculum, but must also have a specialist area. Teachers are involved in trying to develop the individual child's potential to the full.

Leisure Centre Managers

These need a range of business skills, including marketing and publicity, management and leadership, financial and resource management. Leisure Centres offer a wide range of activities and opportunities which the manager organises through the staff.

Professional performers

These get paid for performing, whilst amateurs are not paid directly *(see Amateur or Professional: p.145)*. Both spend a lot of time practising and training to try and become the best. They need ability, determination, and commitment. Rewards can be great, but careers are often short-lived even without injuries.

Groundsmen and women

These are involved in managing the land for sport and recreation, and keeping the surface in the right condition for the activity.

Physiotherapists

These provide treatment to rehabilitate the injured, and advice to prevent injuries. They work with people of all ages, and may be employed in a hospital, and/or have their own private practice.

Journalists

These report sporting events in ways which interest and involve their readers/listeners/viewers. They often start on the local newspaper or radio, and progress on to the national media. Careful observation, and good powers of communication are important.

Coaches

These work with performers of all ages and standards from beginners to professionals. They need to know how to motivate people and to instruct them correctly. They do not necessarily have to have been top performers themselves. Recognised qualifications are awarded by National Governing Bodies. Employment opportunities occur in Leisure Centres, the Youth and Community services, Local Authorities, and in administration in local clubs. In Britain, however, most coaches are unpaid volunteers.

Question Box ?

From what you have read, try to answer these questions.

1 What types of job could be available to you in a Leisure Centre?

2 What qualifications would be of use to you if you worked in a Leisure Centre?

KEYWORDS

- Qualification
- Employment
- Opportunity
- Leisure Industry
- Tourist Industry
- Activity Development
- Injury Rehabilitation and Prevention
- Commerce and Business
- Professional
- P.E. Teacher
- Coach
- Groundsmen and Women
- Physiotherapists
- Journalists
- Managers

CHECK LIST

✔ There are opportunities for employment in many different areas related to P.E. & sport.

✔ In many cases a qualification is needed.

21 NATIONAL ORGANISATIONS AFFECTING PARTICIPATION

The organisation of sport and the arts in the UK is relatively complex and diverse. Many National Organisations affect your participation in physical activities. These include the National Governing Bodies, the Sports Council, the Arts Council, the Countryside Commission, the Central Council of Physical Recreation, and the National Coaching Foundation.

21.1 National Governing Bodies of Sport

The National Governing bodies are responsible for all financial and organisational matters related to their activity. They are independent, administer the rules and regulations, and provide a framework and a focus for their activity. In many sports, the National Governing Bodies of this country were the first in the world, eg. Association Football, Cricket, Rugby Union, etc.

What do They do?

National Governing Bodies of Sport:

- organise awards and training courses for those who wish to take part, coaches, and officials;
- monitor standards, and consider any technical aid that could help officials in their work;
- organise competitions and events, and provide officials for these;
- provide insurance for members;
- administer, monitor, and review disciplinary procedures for those taking part;
- consider rule changes, liaise with international organisations over changes in the rules, and are responsible for informing members of any rule changes.

At national and international levels of competition, national governing bodies:

- organise selection procedures;
- organise various qualifying stages and national championships;
- provide information about these events;
- provide sufficient resources for these processes.

Let's Identify Some

- The British Athletics Federation - **BAF**.
- The British Canoe Union - **BCU**.
- The All England Netball Association - **AENA**.
- The Football Association - **FA**.
- The Rugby Football Union - **RFU**.
- The Lawn Tennis Association - **LTA**.
- The Rugby Football League - **RFL**.
- The British Amateur Gymnastics Association - **BAGA**.
- The Amateur Swimming Association - **ASA**.
- The Royal Yachting Association - **RYA**.
- The Royal and Ancient *(golf)* - **R&A**.
- The Badminton Association of England - **BAE**.

All governing bodies are members of the Central Council of Physical Recreation *(CCPR)*. The governing bodies of Olympic sports are members of the British Olympic Association *(BOA)*.

Links with Schools

Governing bodies can play an important role in developing links with schools. In future, Sports Council grants to national governing bodies will include an assessment of the extent to which they have developed activities for young people, especially in relation to school sport. Governing bodies can help schools with information, posters, videos, coaching assistance, technical assistance, and involvement in inter-school competitions (*'Raising the Game'*, *1995*).

21.2 The Central Council of Physical Recreation *(CCPR)*

The 'Central Council of Recreative Physical Training' was formed in 1935. In 1944, it became the 'Central Council of Physical Recreation'. the aims of which were to:

◆ encourage participation in all types of sporting activities;
◆ provide a forum for the governing bodies of sport.

In 1972 many of its functions, its property, and staff were transferred to the newly formed Government funded Sports Council. The CCPR continued as an independent body for the governing bodies of sport and other representatives, and to continue to promote their aims.

It provides a place for these organisations to discuss various issues, and represents their views. It continues to promote the development of sport and physical recreation, and consults with the Sports Council. The CCPR, through its member bodies, represents over twelve and a half million participants, and over 87 000 groups and clubs. It receives financial support from the Sports Council, members donations, and through the 'Sponsor of Sport' scheme, where financial help is provided by industry.

The CCPR is organised into divisions, namely games and sports, movement and dance, major spectator sports, outdoor pursuits, water recreation, and other interested organisations. These divisions provide common interest groups which meet and discuss current and future issues. The range of issues involved includes sponsorship, coaching services, rules, school and youth sport, playing fields and sports ground provision, and publicity.

CCPR Awards

The CCPR has developed the following Leadership Award schemes, aimed at people who want to develop their confidence and ability in organising groups in games and P.E.

◆ Junior Award *(14-16 years)*.
◆ Community Sports Leaders award *(16+)*.
◆ The Hanson Award, *(18+)*, a higher award.
◆ Basic Expedition Training Award *(BETA)* for those interested in outdoor leadership *(18+)*.

There are tutor training opportunities organised by the CCPR for all these awards. All the awards can be used as part of the Duke of Edinburgh Award Scheme in the service section. Programmes offered by the Youth Sports Trust, especially 'Top Play' and 'Top Sport', could use many of the skills developed in these awards.

Sports Dispute Resolution Panel *(SDRP)*

The Independent Sports Dispute Resolution Panel *(SDRP)* brings together all of the constituent umbrella non-governmental sports bodies through the United Kingdom to work collectively for the greater interests of sportsmen and women.

◆ British Olympic Association
◆ The Central Council of Physical Recreation
◆ Institute of professional Sport
◆ Institute of Sports Sponsorship
◆ Northern Ireland Sports Forum
◆ Scottish Sports Association
◆ Athletes Commission

The greater amounts of money flowing into sport leads to many disputes. Sorting these out in the high courts is extremely costly and takes a very long time, even years. A sporting career is usually relatively short and a sporting talent may be lost whilst the dispute is being resolved. The SDRP provides a framework to avoid delay. The CCPR encourages its members bodies to update their existing disciplinary rules and procedures and adopt SDRP as a part of them.

21.3 The Sports Councils

The original Sports Council was formed by Royal Charter in 1972 to:

◆ promote a general understanding of the social importance, and value of sport and physical recreation;
◆ increase the provision of new sports facilities, and stimulate fuller use of existing facilities;
◆ encourage wider participation in sport and physical recreation as a means of enjoying leisure;
◆ raise standards of sport performance.

Up to 1996 the Sports Council received an annual grant from the government, and all members were appointed by the government. It made grants towards the provision of local community facilities, for special projects, and to governing bodies of sport and others to improve administration, develop participation, and improve standards. It also managed the Lottery Sports Fund in England.

Up to 1996 the Sports Council worked in England through ten regional offices, and these worked closely with other bodies involved in sport in the region. The Sports Council provided the Secretariat to Regional Councils of Sport and Recreation on which most bodies involved in sports development in the region sat. The regional councils produced regional recreation strategies.

On 1st January 1997 the old Sports Council was split into the United Kingdom Sports Council *(UKSC)* and the English Sports Council *(ESC)*. The UKSC took on the responsibilities outlined in their section, and the ESC has the responsibility to carry out all the other duties described in the original 1972 Sports Royal Charter for England. The ten Regional Councils of England were replaced by more informal groups known as Sports Forums, but the ESC continues to work through them.

Scotland, Northern Ireland and Wales have had their own Councils since 1972.

UK Sports Council *(UKSC)*

The UKSC works to put the UK at the forefront of world sport. It sets the framework for sport in the UK and works in partnership with the four Home Country Sports Councils. *(England, Scotland, Northern Ireland and Wales)* as well as with other sports organisations. The UKSC aims to:

◆ produce world class winners in particular sports;
◆ create an athlete focussed system envied the world over;
◆ provide quality assured technical services;
◆ increase the UK's influence on the world stage;
◆ establish a strategic approach to securing major events;
◆ ensure that athletes compete within an ethical environment.

Theses functions are delivered by:

The Performance Development Directorate - the development of sporting excellence of UK teams and athletes on the world stage. The team works with sport's governing bodies to provide funding for performance related programmes.

International Relations and Major Events Directorate - responsible for raising the UK's profile on the world stage by funding British representatives to attend international federation meetings and to develop a strategy to bring major events to these shores.

Ethics and Anti-Doping Directorate - education and comprehensive drug testing programmes are combined to ensure an athlete's right to participate in drug free sport.

The United Kingdom Sports Institute *(UKSI)* - "Performance based, coach driven and athlete focussed" the UKSI is run primarily, but not exclusively, for elite and potentially elite athletes, including disabled athletes. It provides world class services enabling sportsmen and women to achieve success at the highest level of world sport.

The responsibility for developing sport on a home country basis falls to the Home Country Sports Councils

The Home Countries Sports Councils

The home countries sports councils of England, Scotland, Northern Ireland and Wales focus on participation, grass-roots sport and facility development. The aim is to see more people involved in sport, with more places to participate in sport, with all performing to a higher standard. The home countries sports councils are responsible for distributing money from the Lottery Sports Fund.

English Sports Council *(ESC)*

The ESC ensures that the following aims are achieved.

◆ To provide more opportunities and increase participation generally, especially young people through the National Junior Sports Programme (see p.130), improve the education and training of volunteers through the Running Sport programme.

◆ To advise on local development plans and planning applications for playing fields; provide facility design and management advice; support capital projects with grants from the Lottery Sports Fund.

◆ To develop excellence through support to governing bodies of sport; provide specialist facilities at the five National Sports Centres, and in the regional English Network of the United Kingdom Sports Institute; and allocating Lottery Sports Fund revenue to governing bodies and elite individuals.

THE SPORTS COUNCIL FOR WALES

CYNGOR CHWARAEON CYMRU

Past Campaigns

In 1972, the Sports Council began its 'Sport for All' campaign. This continuing campaign aims to encourage people of all ages and abilities to participate in some form of physical activity, increase facilities, and to include local authorities and commercial organisations in developing participation. Target groups have been identified and specific campaigns organised to develop 'Sport for All'.

Sport for All - Come Alive *(1977)*

Sport for All - Disabled People' *(1980/81)* **-** This campaign was part of the 'International Year of Disabled People'. It attempted to promote participation and enjoyment in sport amongst disabled people, and to bring the able bodied and the disabled together. Facilities and access are being improved all the time to help these aims.

50+ All to Play For *(1983/84)* **-** This campaign was launched in 1983, and attempted to increase participation in physical activities for people between 50 - 60. It highlighted the importance of meeting others as well as active participation. An increasingly popular development is 'Prescription Exercise' where Doctors prescribe courses of supervised health-promoting exercise for older people.

Ever thought of Sport *(1985/86)* **-** This campaign was sponsored by Weetabix, and was specifically aimed at 13-24 year olds.

What's your Sport *(1987/88)* **-** This campaign was sponsored by the Milk Marketing Board. The target groups were 13-24 year olds, women, and 45-49 year olds. Advertising on TV invited viewers to send for a 'sports pack'. The names of those who sent for the pack were passed on to local sports councils.

What's your Sport for Women *(1988)* **-** This was part of the 'What's your Sport' campaign, specifically aimed at women.

Milk in Action - Women *(1989)*.

The Year of Sport' *(1991)* **-** This campaign was organised to complement many international events in Britain including the World Student Games.

The Sports Council's National Demonstration Project programme was launched in 1984 to promote mass participation. These campaigns were in line with the developments outlined in two major Sports Council documents which offered strategic direction for British Sport:

◆ Sport in the Community - The next ten years' published in 1982.

◆ Sport in the Community - Into the 90's' published in 1988.

Dulwich Hamlet F.C. community initiative, encouraging grass roots participation from 5 years old upwards.

Sport in the Community - The Next Ten Years

This report identified two, five year periods, and assumed that during these 10 years leisure time would increase. Opportunities had to be created which people would find interesting and could afford. The report focussed on several areas.

Sport in relation to changes in society - population changes, economic changes, and social changes.

Targeting resources - on specific groups that were under-represented *(housewives, disabled, 13-24 and 45-59 year old age groups, etc)*, and the use of promotional campaigns.

Increasing participation - of men in both indoor and outdoor sport by 15%, and women in indoor sport by 70% and outdoor sport by 35%.

Developing new facilities - including 800 sports halls, 50 new and 200 refurbished swimming pools, 3000 new or up-graded sports pitches, and better access to coast and countryside sites.

Developing excellence - through coach education, increasing the number of top level coaches, better planning of coaching schemes, more residential coaching clinics, improving the number and quality of training and competition venues both regionally and nationally, and increasing the efficiency of the administration.

By 1988 the Sports Council found that:

- nearly 1 million extra women had been attracted to indoor sport;
- nearly 600 000 extra men had been attracted to indoor sport;
- 400 000 extra men had been attracted to outdoor sport;
- participation by the middle aged and older people had increased;
- many of the more popular activities were linked to a healthy lifestyle;
- nearly 150 new swimming pools had been built;
- the facilities and management of the National Sports Centres had been greatly improved.

But they also found that:

- the number of women taking part in outdoor sport had fallen;
- less than 400 dry indoor sports facilities had been provided;
- there was still a lack of co-ordination in promoting excellence;
- there were still no National Indoor Arenas;
- some sports still had poor top level facilities;
- resources in general were still inadequate.

Sport in the Community - Into the Nineties

This report identified two groups in society. One group consisted of the generally well-off who were taking advantage of the opportunities available to them. The other group was mainly poor and did not take advantage of 'Sport for All'.

It was also recognised that the development of major facilities depended on the availability of resources; that more co-ordination was needed to make the best use of resources, and that local authorities were best placed to do this. The report emphasised the need to:

Improve participation - including the targeting of young people and women, ethnic minorities, unemployed and the disabled; encouraging more women *(1.25 million)* and men *(750 000)* to participate, and encouraging the provision of more facilities eg. 500 sport halls, 150 swimming pools, improved access to sports sites in the countryside and on water etc.;

Persuade - everyone of all ages to take regular exercise to complement programmes of preventative health care;

Improve excellence - including the encouragement of closer links between coaching, sports medicine and sports science.

Sport in the Nineties: New Horizons

A third document was published in 1993 - 'New Horizons'. This also offered a strategic direction for sport. The Sports Council, as with the previous two strategies, used it as a context for planning the way it would use its resources. It was based on five basic aims. Namely to ensure that young people have the opportunity to acquire sports skills and receive P.E.; to ensure that everyone has the opportunity to participate in sport and physical recreation; to ensure that everyone with interest and ability has the opportunity to improve their standard of performance, and reach the highest standards; and to protect and develop the moral and ethical basis of sport, protect sport and participants from political, commercial and financial exploitation and from practices that are abusive or debasing, including the abuse of drugs.

Bisham Abbey National Sport Centre

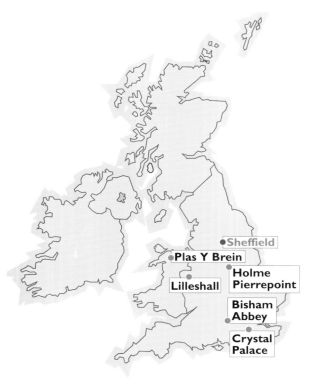

Location of the National Sport Centres and Sheffield, headquarters for The United Kingdom Sports Institute.

National Sports Centres

There are five National Sports Centres. These are:

◆ Bisham Abbey, Buckinghamshire - an indoor and outdoor centre.
◆ Holme Pierrepoint, Nottingham - a national water sports centre.
◆ Lilleshall, Shropshire - an indoor and outdoor centre.
◆ Crystal Palace, London - a multi-sports centre.
◆ Plas y Brenin, North Wales - outdoor activities.

The Sports Council continued to manage the five centres until 1997, when the Sports Council was replaced by the UK Sports Council, and the English Sports Council and the National Centres were transferred to the English Sports Council. The five centres are part of the regional English Network of the United Kingdom Sports Institute.

United Kingdom Sports Institute (UKSI)

In 1997 it was decided by Ministers and the United Kingdom Sports Council that Sheffield would be the headquarters of the new United Kingdom Sports Institute.

Sheffield already had superb sporting facilities as a result of its commitment to invest in sport, leisure and tourism. This led to the World Student Games being held there in 1991, and over 300 major National and International sporting events have been held there since. Many of these facilities are also available for community leisure use.

The decision concluded the first stage of the process to put in place a network of world class sporting facilities throughout the United Kingdom. To finance the new network of facilities which will make up the UKSI some £160 million of National Lottery funding was made available by the Home Country Sports Councils.

It will provide the very best in sports science, medicine, nutrition and coaching expertise and will stimulate an exchange of training techniques across a range of disciplines. The network will include centres of sporting excellence such as Home Country and Regional Institutes (HCRIs) and sports specific academies throughout the UK.

The National Junior Sport Programme

The National Junior Sport Programme involves a partnership between various organisations, including the English Sports Council, the Youth Sport Trust, the National Coaching Foundation, Local Authorities, and Governing Bodies of Sport, to promote quality sport opportunities in schools, the community, and in clubs. The aim of the programme is to coordinate the various schemes and campaigns, and to provide young people with the best opportunities available.

Initiatives include Sportsmark and Sportsmark Gold which offers the chance for a school to show that it values quality P.E. and school sport programmes; Challenge Funding from which a school can benefit from up to £1000 to develop links with sports clubs; Coaching for Teachers which enables teachers to gain new governing body of sport awards; and School Community Sport Initiative which provides, through the Lottery Sports Fund, the opportunity for schools to develop a range of community sporting facilities to benefit young people and the whole community.

Community Sport

A Government Policy Paper 'Raising the Game', 1995, emphasised the role of the Sports Council in England in encouraging the development of sport in schools, and between schools and clubs. They would:

◆ contact schools and provide help and information on sport;
◆ contact clubs and encourage club-school links;
◆ promote school visits by sporting 'stars';
◆ encourage inter-school and inter-regional competitions;
◆ ensure that schools are aware of the opportunities provided by the National Lottery;
◆ keep the National Register of Recreational land, and the Sports Councils facilities database up-to-date;
◆ encourage local businesses to provide sponsorship to schools.

This report indicated that a 'Challenge Fund' would be established by the then Sports Council to promote formal links between local schools, clubs, and governing bodies; and to encourage more young people to play sport. Schools would need to consider their facilities, participation rates, links with governing bodies/clubs, and the number of existing and qualified teachers/coaches, when applying to the fund for support for specialist coaching, coach-training for teachers, and transport.

The Sports Development Continuum Model

In 1993, the Sports Council outlined its Sports Development Continuum model showing how young people could achieve their potential.

Foundation - to develop positive attitudes, basic skills, and the beginnings of knowledge and understanding.
Participation - to encourage the taking part in activities for a variety of reasons *(health, fitness, fun, etc.)*
Performance - to focus on improving standards and developing school-club links.
Excellence - to involve young people in achieving nationally recognised performance standards.

The link between some of the aims of Key Stage 3 and 4, and performance improvement was recognised. Champion Coaching could provide the necessary links between coaches and teachers *(see Champion Coaching, National Coaching Foundation: p.133).*

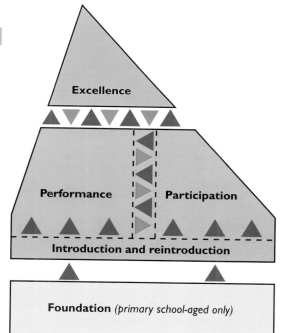

Running Sport

The Running Sport initiative has been developed in partnership with the British Institute of National Sports Administration, the British Olympic Association, the National Coaching Foundation, the National Sports Development Centres, together with the National Sports Councils. The programme is designed to improve the knowledge and skills of every body working in sport, both volunteers and professionals.

The Running Sport programme is made up of a series of short introductory booklets, courses to support these, workshops, and home learning materials covering a range of sports related management skills.

RUNNING SPORT

Action Box

What do you think about the attempt by some able bodied athletes to compete in wheelchair events, on the basis of equal opportunity for all?

1 With the help of your teacher discuss this issue with others in your class.

2 Then vote on the issue.

DISABILITY SPORT ENGLAND

21.4 Disability Sport England (DSE)
formerly (BSAD)

The British Sports Association for the Disabled *(BSAD)* was founded in 1961 by Sir Ludwig Guttmann, a world famous neurosurgeon, to establish a national development and coordinating body for sport and physical recreation for all disabled people in the UK. Although BSAD organised the British Championships, its club base was only in England. The Scottish Sport Association for the Disabled *(SSAD)*, the Welsh Sport Association for the Disabled *(WSAD)*, and Northern Ireland Disability Action exist for the same purpose. Therefore in 1997 BSAD was renamed Disability Sport England *(DSE)*.

They are involved with all disability types, and help with the organisation of sports clubs for the disabled at the local level.

They work with other sport governing bodies in the development of coaching for disabled participants, the provision of award schemes, and the promotion of competitions for the disabled. They act in an advisory way to increase mass and elite participation across various types of disability, to increase mixing with able-bodied sport, and to increase awareness of the sporting achievements of people with disabilities.

Top disabled athletes take part in the special 'Olympics' for the disabled - the Paralympics. Disabled people now often take part in open competitions, and when the disability does not directly affect the performance, there is no reason why they cannot succeed. Although there may still be major problems of access to training facilities and competition, major road running events like the London Marathon are now open to wheelchair athletes.

21.5 National Coaching Foundation (NCF)

The NCF provides education and training services for national governing bodies of sport and sports coaches. Established in 1983, it is an independent company with charitable status. In 1987 the NCF was designated the coaching arm of the Sports Council with responsibility for the coordination of coaching and coach education. The NCF works in partnership with the Scottish Coaching Unit, the Welsh National Coaching Centre, and the Northern Ireland Institute of Coaching. In England its services are organised via its network of ten Coaching Development Officers.

The NCF's main services include:

◆ a wide range of personal development courses and home study packs for coaches of all levels of experience and from all sports *(Coach Development Programme)*;
◆ coaching qualifications *(Introductory Coaching Award, Certificate in Sports Coaching, Diploma in Professional Studies: Sports Coaching)*;
◆ a quality youth sport coaching programme *(Champion Coaching)*;
◆ an information service for key customers *(Supercoach, Inform)*;
◆ a wide range of resources *(books, videos, cassettes)* for all those involved in sport available from the NCF's trading subsidiary *(Coachwise Ltd)*;
◆ a membership service *(National Association of Sports Coaches)*.

The NCF believes that quality coaching is a vital component to the successes achieved by Britain's top performers and is dedicated to the development of sports coaching by helping to produce better coaches. The NCF represents UK coach education on the International Council for Coach Education *(ICCE)*.

Champion Coaching

Champion Coaching was established in 1991, as a one year pilot project funded directly by the Government, and managed by the National Coaching Foundation. It provides sports coaching for children in after-school hours. The outcome of the initial 24 pilot projects emphasised that for any successful development to take place in young people's sport programmes they had to be delivered within a coordinated structure, where schools, clubs, local authorities, coaches and young people worked together, and that there had to be a significant increase in the number of local coaches who were qualified and able to work with young people.

Champion Coaching depends on partnerships which have been developed between the National Coaching Foundation, the Sports Councils of England, Wales, and Northern Ireland, the National Governing Bodies of Sport, the British Sport Association for the Disabled, the Youth Sport Trust, Local Authority and Education Departments, Schools, and Clubs.

Champion Coaching has grown and in 1996 there were 90 schemes in England, Wales, and Northern Ireland involving 145 local authorities, 17 sports governing bodies, over 2500 coaches, and 20 000 young people.

Champion Coaching aims to help create, develop, and support links between local authorities, governing bodies, schools, and clubs to:

◆ create quality coaching opportunities for 11 - 16 year olds;
◆ support these young people's progression from school sport to junior clubs and squads;
◆ support the development of junior clubs and their coaches;
◆ to recruit and develop sports coaches.

Each scheme identifies a local Youth Sport Manager who coordinates all the key agencies involved. Each programme of sport lasts for at least 7 weeks and a minimum of 20 hours.

21.6 The Youth Sport Trust (YST)

The Youth Sport Trust is a registered charity. It is supported by Loughborough University and the private sector, and works in partnership with the Sports Councils and the National Coaching Foundation. It aims to develop quality sport programmes for 4–18 year olds, which are run at local level, and coordinated at national level.

The Trust wants children to have:

◆ fun and success in sport;
◆ top coaching and resources;
◆ an introduction to sport suited to their own level of development;
◆ the opportunity to develop a range of sport skills;
◆ the chance to develop good sporting attitudes;
◆ positive competition;
◆ a sound foundation for lifelong physical activity. *(YST 1995)*

There are four **TOP** programmes which are part of the National Junior Sports Programme:

◆ TOP Play for 4–9 year olds *(fun and core games)*;
◆ TOP Sport for 7–11 year olds *(sport/games introductions)*;
◆ Champion Coaching for 11–16 year olds *(see p.133)*;
◆ TOP Club *(developing opportunities through clubs for all children)*.

The emphasis in all these programmes is on quality of training, resources, programme development, and the promotion of an active healthy lifestyle, and lifelong participation.

('Bringing Sport to Life for Young People' YST, 1995).

21.7 The Sports Aid Foundation (SAF)

The SAF was established in 1976. It is an independent fund raising organisation dedicated to the development of excellence, and the encouragement of talent. It awards grants to leading performers in sport to help them compete in top international events, including the Olympic Games.

The SAF Charitable Trust was formed in 1984 to help sportspeople with disabilities, and promising young performers. Between 1976 and 1996, the SAF distributed over £13 million in training grants. It currently aids about 3000 competitors in 50 different sports.

SAF is supported by individuals, industry, and commerce, charities, clubs, and associations. It raises money from donations, fund raising events, donor grants, legacies, and joint promotions. For the first time, it received Government assistance in 1995/96 through the Sport Council's 'Atlanta Fund' to help prepare potential Olympic competitors for the Games.

Applications for grants are made through the National Governing Bodies. Financial help can be given for competition, preparation, and training costs.

There are nine regional offices in England, and associated SAF companies also exist in Scotland, Wales, and Northern Ireland. The regional offices raise funds locally to support sportspeople in their area who do not receive a national SAF grant, but show potential for the future.

21.8 The National Association of Sports Coaches (NASC)

NASC was formed by the merging of the British Institute of Sports Coaches and the National Coaching Foundation. NASC is designed to give sports coaches the opportunity to become part of the wider family of coaches, and to offer them a chance to learn form the huge amount of coaching expertise that exists in this country. NASC works to:

- promote the status of qualified coaches;
- promote and protect the interests and welfare of all coaches;
- influence national policies for coaches and coaching;
- set and safeguard standards in coaching;
- ensure quality in coaching;
- promote and safeguard the interest and welfare of all performers through quality coaching;
- provide a benefits package to meet members needs.

21.9 The Countryside Commission (CC)

The Countryside Commission was established in 1968, in place of the National Parks Commission, its duties being to conserve the natural beauty of the countryside of England and to improve and extend opportunities for people to enjoy it, balancing conservation and accessibility to the public.

Chairman and Commissioners are appointed by the Secretary of State for the Environment, funding coming from the Department of the Environment - most being invested directly in the countryside in the form of grants and project work.

The Commission develops policies that benefit the countryside and seeks to persuade others to put those policies into action. It advises government and Parliament on countryside matters, as well as being responsible for designating National Parks and Areas of Outstanding Natural Beauty, defining Heritage Coasts, and establishing National Trails for walkers and riders.

The National Parks include the North York Moors, the Yorkshire Dales, the Peak District, Dartmoor, and the Lake District. The Commission is active in seven main areas of work:

- granting aid to promote recreation and conservation;
- identifying national trails, heritage coasts, and national parks;
- advising government, and others, on countryside policy;
- advising on recreation and conservation management techniques;
- researching on the impact on the countryside of all the different activities for which it is used;
- experimenting with management methods for recreation and conservation;
- promoting an understanding of the countryside.

Major initiatives currently involving the Commission include the establishing of 12 Community Forests on the edges of towns and cities and a commitment to fully opening the footpath and bridleway network by the year 2000.

Learning to sail on Ullswater in the Lake District.

THE **ARTS COUNCIL** OF ENGLAND

21.10 The Arts Council *(AC)*

In 1994 the Arts Council of England, the Scottish Arts Council, and the Arts Council of Wales were created from the Arts Council of Great Britain *(founded 1946)*. The Arts Council of Northern Ireland already existed. The Aims of the Arts Council of England are:

- to increase the opportunities for people to enjoy the arts;
- to develop knowledge, understanding, and practice of the arts;
- co-operate with government and other organisations to achieve its objectives.

It receives a grant from the government and National Lottery money, distributing the money through 10 Regional Arts Boards. In Dance, it funds and subsidises touring work, research and development, choreographical development, festivals, and the production of dance videos for education.

21.11 The International Olympic Committee *(IOC)*

The IOC organises the Olympic Games, and determines the rules under which the Olympics will be held. The IOC is charged with upholding the spirit of the Olympic Ideal *(see Participation, Excellence and the Olympic Ideal: p.138)*. The IOC seeks to:

- educate young people through sport and promote a spirit of understanding;
- spread the Olympic ideal throughout the world;
- bring together performers every four years for an international festival of sport – the Olympic Games *(Summer and Winter)*.

21.12 The British Olympic Association *(BOA)*

The BOA, formed in 1905, is the National Olympic Committee for Great Britain. It is completely independent of Government and only subject to the rules of the IOC. All Olympic sports are represented on the BOA, and the BOA represents British interests on the International Olympic Committee *(IOC)*. It raises money for British teams taking part in the summer and winter Olympics, and it is also involved with meetings on sports medicine *(it runs the British Olympic Medical Centre in London)*, team preparation, team management, and Olympic education.

The aims of the BOA are:

- to encourage interest in the Olympic Games, and to foster the aims and ideals of the Olympic movement;
- to organise British participation in the Olympic Games;
- to assist National Governing Bodies in the preparation of their competitors for the Olympic Games;
- to provide for consultation among the national governing bodies of all Olympic sports;

British Paralympics logo. The Paralympics are not part of the Olympic movement, but organise and run events dedicated to elite disabled sport, independently and in parallel with the Olympics.

Question Box ?

From what you have read, try to answer these questions.

1 What are the National Governing Bodies responsible for?

2 What are the aims of the NCF?

3 What does the IOC do?

CHECK LIST

✔ *National Governing Bodies are responsible for all matters related to their activity.*

✔ *The C.C.P.R. provides a forum for the National Governing Bodies to discuss various issues, & it represents their views.*

✔ *The Sports Councils try to increase participation, increase facilities, & improve excellence.*

✔ *Schools, clubs and governing bodies should develop links between them.*

✔ *United Kingdom Sports Institute consists of a network of facilities including the 5 National Sports Centres, with the headquarters in Sheffield.*

✔ *D.S.E. advises on sport for the disabled.*

✔ *The N.C.F. helps develop sports coaching. It started the 'Champion Coaching' scheme in 1991.*

✔ *The 'Youth Sport Trust' is about 'Bringing Sport to Life for Young People'.*

✔ *N.A.S.C. is an association of sports coaches.*

✔ *The S.A.F. provides financial help for leading performers in sport.*

✔ *The Countryside Commission has to balance conservation & public accessibility for recreation.*

✔ *Arts Councils financially support Dance.*

✔ *The I.O.C. organises the Olympic Games & promotes the Olympic Ideal.*

✔ *The B.O.A. represents Britain on the I.O.C..*

KEYWORDS

- National Governing Bodies
- Central Council of Physical Recreation
- The Sports Dispute Resolution Panels
- The Sports Councils
- Sport in the Community - The Next Ten Years
- Sport in the Community - Into the Nineties
- New Horizons
- National Sports Centres
- United Kingdom Sports Institute
- The National Junior Sport Programme
- The Sports Development Continuum Model
- Running Sport
- Disability Sport England
- The National Coaching Foundation
- Champion Coaching
- The Youth Sport Trust
- The Sports Aid Foundation
- The National Association of Sport Coaches
- The Countryside Commission
- The Arts Councils
- International Olympic Committee
- British Olympic Association

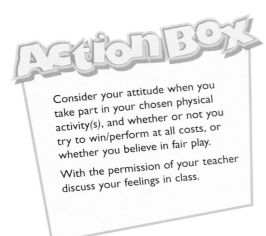

One of the Olympic Torches carried in relay from Olympia to the 1948 Games held in London.

22 PARTICIPATION, EXCELLENCE & THE OLYMPIC IDEAL

Participation and the development of excellence, are important aims in Physical Education and Physical Recreation. They are also at the heart of the Olympic movement and the Olympic ideal. Let's look at the aims and ideals of the Olympic movement.

22.1 The Aims & Ideals of the Olympics

The aims of the Olympic movement are to:

◆ promote the development of those physical and moral qualities which are the basis of sport;
◆ educate young people through sport in a spirit of friendship, helping to build a better and more peaceful world;
◆ spread the Olympic principles throughout the world, thereby creating international goodwill;
◆ bring together the athletes of the world in a great festival of sport every four years.

The games are awarded to cities *(not countries)*, and are designed to be competitions where all the competitors have an equal chance, and share in the spirit of sportsmanship. Discrimination is rejected, and equal opportunity for all emphasised. Competitors should not receive any financial reward for taking part. The International Governing body of each sport decides who is eligible to compete under the rules of the sport *(see Amateur/professional: p.145)*.

The Olympic Ideal

The Olympic Ideal is an outlook on life which includes the enjoyment of taking part, trying hard, fair play, respect for the rules, and the pursuit of excellence. This idea of the pursuit of excellence is contained in the Olympic motto; '**Citius, Altius, Fortius**', which means 'Fastest, Highest, Strongest'.

The Five Ringed Olympic Flag - The five ringed Olympic flag was decided upon in 1913. The rings symbolise the unity of the five continents. The colours are blue, black, red, yellow, and green. At least one of these colours is part of the flag of each member country. It was first flown in 1920 at Antwerp. During the opening ceremony, the head of state of the host nation is invited to open the games. All the teams parade around the stadium with the host nation last.

The Olympic Flame - The Olympic torch is lit from the rays of the sun at Olympia in Greece, and is carried by a relay of runners from Olympia to the the arena where the Olympic flame is lit, and burns throughout the Games.

The Olympic Oath - The Olympic Oath, which is set out below, is repeated by one chosen representative during the opening ceremony.
"We swear that we will take part in these Olympic Games in the true spirit of sportsmanship, and that we will abide by the rules that govern them, for the glory of sport and the honour of our country."

Action Box

Consider your attitude when you take part in your chosen physical activity(s), and whether or not you try to win/perform at all costs, or whether you believe in fair play.

With the permission of your teacher discuss your feelings in class.

22.2 The Ancient Olympic Games

The ancient games were held for over 1000 years in the valley of Olympia beside the river Kladeos in ancient Greece.

The games were held every four years from 776 BC to AD *(or Modern Era (ME))* 393. Warring city states often called a truce to take part in the games. A great statue of Zeus was said to be the centrepiece of the Games which were basically a religious festival. A sacred olive tree grew beside the temple of Zeus, and its leaves were used to make the crowns which were awarded to the winners. The early games consisted of only a few races, but gradually other events were added, including wrestling, boxing, and throwing the javelin and discus.

Only 'free' men *(not slaves)* and boys could participate. 'The Heraia' *(the unmarried women's games)*, were held separately. Married women were not allowed to watch the male games.

The games declined when the attitude of 'win at all costs' and corruption spread.

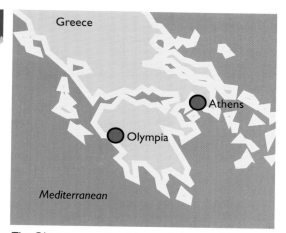

The Olympics was the oldest and biggest athletic festival in ancient Greece and continued to be held once every four years for ten centuries.

In the 4th Century AD Olympia was hit by earthquakes, then it was buried in silt by flooding. We know a lot about the original Olympic Games because the Greeks at the time wrote about it, which helps archaeologists work out how all the buildings were used. **1** Religious garden with Alters, Temples & sacred olive tree. **2** Prytaneion, where winners' feasts were held and the sacred fire of Hestia was kept burning, day & night. The first event of the Games was a relay using torches, the honour of lighting the fire of Hestia went to the winners and their torch. **3** Competitors entrance tunnel into the stadium, this has survived. **4** The stade *(stadium)*, 192.8m sand running track with stone start & finish lines, also still there! **5** The Gymnasium, where Javelin & Discus events took place and the athletes lived. It had an indoor two lane running track also 192.8m long. **6** The Palaistra, used for jumping, wrestling, and training. **7** Bathing houses, after exercise the Greeks always bathed. **8** Olympia even had a Swimming Pool. **9** This wall was built to keep the river Kladeos at bay. **10** The Leonidaion, a hotel for important guests attending the Games. **11** The Hippodrome for horse and chariot racing, with starting stalls controlled by a mechanical golden dolphin. Chariot racing was sponsored by rich horse breeders, winning helped sell 'their' horses. **12** Banks, money became increasingly important.

PLAN OF OLYMPIA

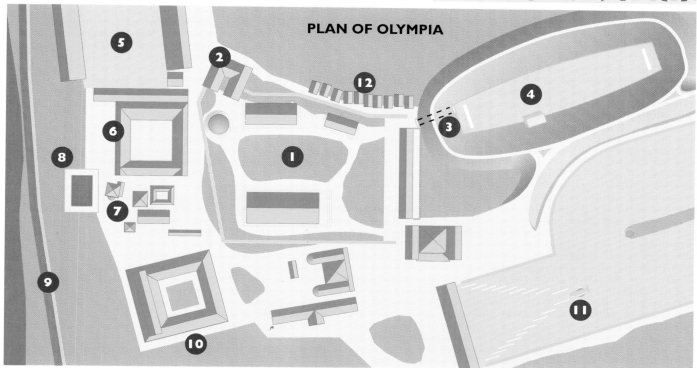

22.3 The Modern Summer Olympics

In 1894, Baron Pierre De Coubertin organised an international conference to discuss the possibility of restarting the games. They decided that the first modern games would be held in Athens *(Greece)* in 1896. They formed the International Olympic Committee, and also decided that the games would be held every four years, each time in a different country. Money had to be raised to build the facilities in Greece. Over 50 000 people watched the opening ceremony where a lighted torch, carried by a team of runners from the valley of Olympia, was brought into the stadium. The torchbearer climbed a few steps and the eternal flame was lit. The Olympic hymn was sung by a choir, and competitors from 13 countries paraded around the stadium. Venues since then are set out below.

Paris 1900, St Louis 1904, London 1908, Stockholm 1912, Antwerp 1920, Paris 1924, Amsterdam 1928, Los Angeles 1932, Berlin 1936, London 1948, Helsinki 1952, Melbourne 1956, Rome 1960, Tokyo 1964, Mexico City 1968, Munich 1972, Montreal 1976, Moscow 1980, Los Angeles 1984, Seoul 1988, Barcelona 1992, Atlanta 1996, Sydney 2000, and Athens 2004.

Jane Torville and Christopher Dean performing their famous 'Bolero' dance routine which scored full marks at the Winter Olympics in Sarajevo 1984.

22.4 The Winter Olympic Games

For many years, winter sports were not included in the games. In 1920, ice-hockey, figure skating and skiing were included. These sports proved to be so popular that the IOC organised a separate games for winter sports in 1924. These first Winter Games included ski-jumping, cross country skiing, and bobsledding. Since then the number of sports has increased, and now also includes downhill and slalom skiing, first introduced in 1948, and the biathlon which combines cross country skiing with rifle shooting.

The IOC recently took the decision to spread the summer and winter games, and alternate them every two years.

The 1994 games in Lillehammer, Norway, emphasised environmental considerations; the facilities were built of local wood and stone to blend into their surroundings. Energy-saving materials were used wherever possible, and the packaging of Olympic products, which excluded environmentally harmful substances, was kept to a minimum. Approximately 2.2 million people visited the town, and a 1000 competitors took part. In Nagano 1998, Snowboarding, Curling, and Women's Ice Hockey were added to the list of events.

Venues for the Winter Games are set out below;

Chamonix 1924, St Morritz 1928, Lake Placid 1932, Garmisch-Partenkirchen 1936, St Morritz 1948, Oslo 1952, Cortina 1956, Squaw Valley 1960, Innsbruck 1964, Grenoble 1968, Sapporo 1972, Innsbruck 1976, Lake Placid 1980, Sarajevo 1984, Calgary 1988, Albertville 1992, Lillehammer 1994, Nagano 1998, and Salt Lake City, 2002.

22.5 Participation & Excellence

Just taking part in the Olympics represents a tremendous achievement. A few performers win Olympic medals. The ideas of taking part, and excellence are associated with the Olympic Games as well as with other major events. Most of us remember, or have read about a few outstanding performances that are special. Let's identify a few of them.

In 1936 *(Berlin)*, Jessie Owens *(USA)* won the 100 metres, 200 metres, Long Jump and was part of the winning '4 x 100' metres relay squad. This feat of winning 4 track and field golds remained unequalled until Fanny Blankers Koen *(Holland)* won the 100 metres, 200 metres, 80 metres Hurdles and the long jump at the 1948 Games in London. Carl Lewis *(USA)* repeated Jessie Owens' achievements at the Los Angeles Games in 1984.

Emile Zatopek *(Czechoslovakia)* was an outstanding long distance runner in the 1948 Olympics *(London)* where he won the 10 000 metres and came second in the 5000 metres *(after a tactical blunder)*, and in the 1952 Helsinki Olympics where he won gold medals in the 10 000 metres and the 5000 metres in new Olympic records, and the Marathon *(42 kilometres, 26miles 385 yards)*.

In 1960 *(Rome)*, a barefoot Abebe Bikila *(Ethiopia)* won the Marathon, and repeated the win in 1964, but this time wearing shoes.

In 1968 *(Mexico City)* Bob Beamon *(USA)* shattered the Olympic Long Jump record by jumping 8.90 metres *(over 29 feet)* - albeit at an altitude of over 7000 feet where the thinner air helps the jumps and the throws. This distance was not beaten until the 1991 Athletic World Championships in Tokyo by Mike Powell *(USA)*,after a titanic struggle with Carl Lewis.

Also at the 1968 games, Dick Fosbury *(USA)* astonished the world with a new High Jump technique, the 'Fosbury Flop', won the gold medal and broke the Olympic record.

In 1972 *(Munich)* Mark Spitz *(USA)* won 7 gold medals, and became the greatest swimmer in history. Also in 1972, Lasse Viren *(Finland)*, won the 5000 metres, and 10 000 metres track double, a feat he repeated in 1976 in Montreal *(Canada)*.

Al Oerter *(USA)*, a discus thrower, is the only Olympic athlete to win a gold medal in 4 consecutive Olympics so far *(1956, 60, 64, & 68)*. At each competition he broke his own Olympic record.

Olga Korbut, a Russian gymnast, charmed the world and won two gold medals in the 1972 Olympics. In 1976 she found herself up against a 14 year old Romanian gymnast called Nadia Comaneci. Nadia won 2 golds scoring the perfect 10 in both the Beam and the Asymmetrical bars. On the track, Ed Moses *(USA)* won the 400 metres Hurdles in an Olympic record time, establishing a dominance in this event for many years afterwards.

In Moscow *(1980)*, Steve Ovett *(GB)* won the 800 metres, with Sebastian Coe *(GB)* second *(another example of a tactical blunder)*; and Coe won the 1500 metres *(but in a time slower than Herb Elliot's World and Olympic record in Rome in 1960)* with Ovett third. Mirus Yifter *(Ethiopia)* won the 5000 metres and 10 000 metres double, after many previous disappointments.

Zatopek 1955

Dick Fosbury winning the gold medal, Mexico City 1968

Mark Spitz 1972 Munich Olympics

Action Box

1 Identify the performers you have most enjoyed watching on television at recent Olympic Games.

2 With your teacher's permission compare your list with others in your class

3 Try to explain why you liked these individuals so much.

Question Box ?

From what you have read, try to answer these questions.

1 What is the Olympic Ideal?

2 What is the Olympic Oath?

3 Who is credited with restarting the modern Olympic Games?

4 When was the first separate Winter Games held?

KEYWORDS

- Olympic Games
- Aims
- Ideals
- Olympism
- Motto
- Flag
- Torch
- Oath
- Stade
- Zeus
- Heraia
- Ancient Games
- Modern Games
- Pierre de Coubertin
- Summer Games
- Winter Games
- Participation
- Excellence

Since 1952 several boxers from the USA have won Olympic golds and then become World heavyweight champions. These include Floyd Patterson *(1952)*, Muhammad Ali *(1960)*, Joe Frazier *(1964)*, and George Foreman *(1968)*, who regained a version of the World title in 1994.

In the 1956 Winter Games *(Cortina d'Ampezzo)* Anton Sailer *(Austria)* won gold medals in the Giant Slalom, the Special Slalom, and the Downhill ski race. Not until 1968 did Jean Claude Killy *(France)*, equal this record.

In 1964 *(Innsbruck)* Lidija Skoblikova *(USSR Russia)* won 4 gold medals in all four Speed Skating events; the 500 metres, 1000 metres, 1500 metres and the 3000 metres. This was the first time this had been achieved.

In Sarajevo, Bosnia *(1984)*, Jane Torvill and Christopher Dean *(GB)* scored the perfect six for their winning 'Bolero' Ice Dancing routine.

Many competitors have had to overcome serious problems to become Olympic champions. Wilma Rudolph *(USA)* was very ill when she was young, suffering from polio, and could not walk properly until she was seven years old. In Rome *(1960)* she won gold medals in the 100 metres, 200 metres, and in the '4 x 100' metres relay squad.

The competitors mentioned above, and many others, have thrilled and enthralled audiences over the years.

The Olympics are all about taking part, excellence, and fair play. They are supposed to be free from political pressure, discrimination, corruption, financial gain, and cheating. The performers are expected to live up to the Olympic Ideal; the ancient Games declined when the true spirit was lost. The modern Games have existed for a much shorter period, and the pressure on performers today is huge. What will happen to the Games and the Olympic Ideal in the future? What has happened to them already?

CHECK LIST

✔ The Olympic Ideal is expressed in the concept of Olympism.

✔ The Olympic flag is made of five rings. Its colours are blue, black, red, yellow & green.

✔ The Olympic Oath is repeated by one representative of the movement during the opening ceremony.

✔ The Ancient Olympic games were held for over 1000 years in the valley of Olympia, Greece.

✔ Only 'Free' men and boys could participate.

✔ 'The Heraia', the unmarried women's games, were held separately.

✔ The Modern Summer Olympic Games were first held in Athens in 1896.

✔ Baron Pierre de Coubertin is credited with restarting the Games.

✔ A separate Winter Games was first held in 1924.

✔ The Olympic spirit emphasises both participation & excellence.

23 ISSUES AFFECTING PARTICIPATION

There are many issues that affect participation in physical recreational activities. They include opportunities for women to take part, the amateur/professional debate, sponsorship, the media, doping, racist behaviour, and politics.

23.1 Women in Sport

Departu Tulu of Ethiopia beats Paula Radcliffe of England into second place in the 1997 IAAF World Cross Country Championships, Turin.

Women have traditionally been associated with the arts in general, and dance in particular, but many sporting and adventurous activities have traditionally been seen as male pursuits.

Women have excelled in many sports. One recent example is in women's Rugby Union. England won the second World Cup in 1994, beating 22 countries. The Womens Amateur Rugby Football Union was formed in 1983 with twelve UK clubs. In 1994, there were enough clubs for national leagues to be formed. England has five divisions. Some schools are beginning to offer Rugby and Football to girls. One of the greatest athletes of all time of either sex was Beryl Burton *(1937-96)* the British Cyclist, who beat the best of the men.

The Sports Council in 'Women and Sport - Policy and Frameworks for Action' emphasise two principles in its 'Better Quality Sport for All' strategy. These are:

◆ sports development - for progression, participation and excellence;
◆ sports equity - fairness in sport, equality of opportunity, and to deal with inequality of opportunity caused by prejudice.

Action Box

1 Describe how you feel about the way women seem to have been held back in many sports.

2 With your teacher's help set up a discussion and listen to the ideas of others in your class.

3 Try to imagine your feelings if you were discriminated against.

The Sex Discrimination Act, 1975, makes sex discrimination unlawful in employment, training, education, and the provision of goods, facilities and services. If a man, because of his gender, is treated more favourably than a woman, then sex discrimination is considered to have happened. However, competitive sport is excluded by section 44 which allows for separate competitions on the grounds of strength and physique. Even so there have been several cases brought by women in sport alleging discrimination, including performers and coaches in both professional and amateur sports.

Why is it that women have been restricted in this way? This issue is part of the traditional view of the role of women in society as housewives. Their lack of financial independence; the lack of child care facilities, and their supposed 'unsuitability' for certain types of competitive physical sport have all worked together to restrict their participation. These cultural barriers are deeply rooted and also affect the coverage of womens sport by the media, potential commercial sponsorship opportunities, and opportunities for womens participation and progression.

The image that many women have of sport and their relative lack of self-confidence similarly creates a negative attitude. Black and Asian women, and women with disabilities encounter further problems which seriously limit the opportunities available to them, and restrict their access to sport.

Emma Mitchel gets the ball out during an England v Wales, Womens' International Rugby match held at Leicester 1995.

Australia wins Women's Cricket World Cup 1997

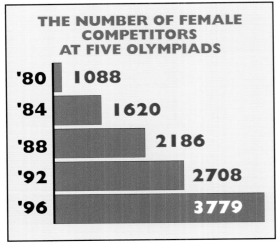

After Runners World

Sports Council Campaigns

Sports Councils' campaigns have targeted women, and attempted to increase their participation rates and promote excellence. Some success has occurred *(see Sports Council: p.126)* in indoor sports, but in outdoor sport, especially team games, women's participation has decreased. The General Household Survey, 1990, indicated that the most popular women's physical activities include walking *(38%)*, aerobics and keep fit activities *(16%)*, swimming *(13%)*, cycling *(7%)*, snooker *(5%)*, and darts *(4%)*.

Equal Opportunities for Women

It is important that women receive equality of opportunity in all areas of sport as performers, coaches, officials, and administrators. Women need the confidence to develop their sporting potential, and require support to do this and to progress in whatever area they are involved. The Womens Sports Foundation *(WSF)* a national voluntary organisation, was set up in 1984 to promote women in sport.

Women and the Olympics

Although unmarried women had their separate games in ancient Greece, the modern Games were based on male competition, with de Courbetin stating that the role of women should be restricted to that of the admiring spectator. Gender is missing from the list of categories identified as possible causes of discrimination.

"No discrimination is allowed against any country or person on grounds of race, religion, or politics."

Women were not allowed to compete in the 1896 Games, and were only allowed to participate in Golf and Tennis at the Games of 1900. Gradually the number of events in which they could compete increased with swimming events in 1912, and athletic events in 1928 *(in 1922 the International Women's Sports Federation organised a one day Womens 'Olympics' in Paris)*. Despite the strong tradition of women's hockey, it was not included in the Games until 1980. At the 1968 Mexico games, a woman, Enriqueta Basilio, lit the Olympic flame, the first woman to do so.

Women were eventually allowed to run the marathon in 1984 and the 10 000 metres in 1988, and to take part in seven judo events in 1992. However in 1992, women were still excluded from many events including Boxing, Wrestling, Ice-Hockey, Water Polo, and Weight-Lifting.

Women were allowed to compete in the Winter Olympics from their start in 1924, but only in a restricted number of events, for example they were not allowed to compete in Speed Skating until 1960.

Many British women have had success at the Olympics, including Anita Lonsborough 200 metre Breast Stroke gold medalist *(1960)*; Mary Rand, Long Jump gold, and Ann Packer, 800 metres gold and 400 metres silver *(1964)*; Mary Peters Pentathlon gold *(1972)*; Tessa Sanderson Javelin gold *(1984)*, and Sally Gunnell 400 metres Hurdles gold *(1992)*.

23.2 Amateur or Professional

De Coubertin wanted the Olympics to be a festival of amateur sport, where the performers took part without payment. In London *(1908)* a sermon was preached in St Paul's Cathedral in which it was emphasised that the important thing about the Games was *"less to win than to take part in them."* The 19th century and early 20th century view was that this idea could only really be followed by amateurs. Amateurs receive no financial reward, and it was thought therefore that they would be less likely to cheat and be corrupted. The Professionals used trainers and coaches, and because they received payment, they were thought to be more open to corruption. These feelings gave rise to three main fears in the 19th Century, namely that:

◆ payment would lead to cheating;
◆ professionals would out–class amateurs;
◆ idea of 'gentlemanly' or sporting conduct would be lost.

The issue of amateur or professional status divided the Olympic family for many years until the IOC decided to allow the individual Governing Bodies to decide who was qualified *(eligible)* to compete in the games. The IOC now emphasises eligibility *(rule 45)* rather than amateur or professional status.

It is argued that the 19th century fears are unjustified and unfair to professionals. In general, professionals are no more corrupt than amateurs; amateur sport is even more popular now than it was, and sportsmanship depends on the individual. No-one can be directly paid for participating in the Olympic Games, but today 'amateurs' have trust funds, are sponsored, and have agents.

In Seoul *(1988)* professional basketball players, amateur athletes, professional tennis players, and amateur gymnasts and boxers all participated. Many people do not agree with these developments, and feel that the Olympic movement has been tarnished. Others believe that the Olympic movement must change with the times.

The Two Rugby Codes

There used to be a clear distinction between Rugby Union *(amateur)* and Rugby League *(professional)*. The history of these two rugby codes reflects 19th Century beliefs about amateurism and professionalism. Recently Rugby Union has decided to allow players to be paid for playing, in effect ending the amateur/professional division between the two codes. Smaller Rugby Union clubs are worried that they might not be able to afford such payments. International players have welcomed this change in the rules. The relationship between Rugby Union and Rugby League is changing, there is increasing cooperation between them, and people are discussing whether the two will ever come together. In 1996 the top Rugby Union club *(Bath)* and the top Rugby League club *(Wigan)* played each other in two games, one under League rules, and the other under Union rules.

Action Box

1 With your teacher's permission discuss if you think professionalism has spoilt sport in general.

2 With your teacher's permission discuss the advantages of amateur sport.

3 Then make a list of the advantages of each.

23.3 Commercialisation & Sponsorship

Sports events, and adventurous activities, etc. cost money to organise. One way to generate income and to help meet the costs is to involve commercial interests. The process of organising an event or performance along business lines is called commercialisation.

The Olympic Games provide a good example of the process of commercialisation at work. In the 1904 *(St Louis)* Olympics, commercial displays of farm machinery helped towards the costs. Even in the American depression of the 1930's, the Los Angeles Olympics made a small profit through commercial advertising.

The Olympic Games are seen as major 'prestige' events by the host cities, and costs have increased as each city has tried to out do previous Games and present its best image to the world. The 1980 Olympics in Moscow cost involved over 200 officially endorsed products - that is companies paid to be allowed to have the Olympic logo on their products.

Mainly because of increasing costs, only Los Angeles applied to be host city for the 1984 Summer Games. The Olympic charter requires the host city to be responsible for all costs, but the Los Angeles city authorities refused to be liable. Eventually the Games' finances were made the shared responsibility of the US Olympic Committee, and a non-profit making private company. This led to the formation of the Los Angeles Organising Committee, which decided to organise a privately funded Olympics. Companies involved included Coca Cola, IBM, and McDonalds. The Games made a large profit. In 1988, the IOC allowed a private company, International Sport and Leisure, to negotiate the sponsorship deals. Sponsorship is a major part of the commercialisation process.

The National Lottery

Money can be raised for sporting events in many ways, including donations, fees, and sponsorship. In Britain the National Lottery raises money through instant scratch card games and weekly draws. The National Lottery is run by a private company *(Camelot)*, although the scheme was set up by the Government, with the Department of Heritage having responsibility for it.

The Arts Councils and the Sports Councils for England, Scotland, Wales, and Northern Ireland, are responsible for distributing the funds in their areas. The Government is emphasising the chance for schools to bid for lottery money to improve facilities, build new facilities, and buy equipment.

Every pound of National Lottery money produces 28p to spend on good causes. The Sports Council's Lottery Unit distributes money for the development of talented athlete's, major international events, and coaching and leadership programmes. The Lottery Sports Fund assists talented individuals and teams to improve their international ranking and win more medals in international competitions.

Advantages and Disadvantages

When sponsorship is provided, money *(or other material goods)* is given to an activity, event, organisation, performance, or individual(s), by the sponsor, and in return the receiver of the sponsorship advertises the sponsors' products. The sponsors get a relatively cheap form of mass advertising which they hope will improve sales and create goodwill towards them and their products. They hope to become better known, and linked in people's minds with the image of the activity, which in the case of sport is seen to be healthy, fair, and about keeping to the rules.

However, it has been suggested that, such 'background' advertising is ineffective because people forget the product after a while, and take the sponsors name for granted! Tobacco companies and Brewers actively sponsor many sporting events and activities. Many people disagree with this because it associates products that cause disease *(cancer, heart disease, bronchitis etc)* with 'healthy' activities. The British Amateur Gymnastics Association has a policy of not using alcohol or tobacco companies as sponsors. In France the alcoholic drinks industry is prohibited from sponsoring sport. This led to problems with a major american sponsor *(brewers)* of the 1998 Football World Cup Tournament as the finals were held in France.

In 1997 the government stated that tobacco sponsorship of sport would be banned once existing agreements had been completed.

If controversial things happen that cause a lot of bad publicity, such as drug misuse *(see Doping: p.149)*, sponsors may decide that the negative image will harm their products, and withdraw their sponsorship.

Most sponsors prefer to sponsor 'stars', potential 'stars', popular activities or important events. For those receiving sponsorship, there is an immediate boost to their income, which provides them with better long term, as well as short term opportunities. The sponsored sport could also receive more publicity, an increase in public awareness of the activity, an increase in the number of people wanting to participate in the activity, more facilities, and better equipment.

When sponsorship is obtained, the structure of the activity often adapts to the finances available, and becomes dependent on the sponsorship to maintain itself. For example motor racing would probably survive without the massive amounts of sponsorship it receives, but not in its present form.

The requirements of sponsors are increasingly influencing the organisation of events. In the USA, advertising 'breaks' on TV and Radio allow sponsors to remind audiences of their products. The more 'breaks', the better as far as the sponsors are concerned.

Sponsors want value for money, and they have to check if this is being achieved. They check the amount of publicity received, and the product sales. Some companies are beginning to question whether sponsorships are the most efficient ways of getting value for money.

The Sportsmatch Scheme

This Government scheme tries to encourage private firms to support local sports events and projects. Such sponsorship can earn tax relief, that is the sponsors do not have to pay tax on the money provided. The sponsors money is matched by government money.

In England, the scheme is run by the Institute of Sports Sponsorship *(ISS)* which channels money to local sport and schools-related sporting projects. In addition the Sports Councils have been asked to make the encouragement of more business sponsorship in schools a priority. There are various ways in which the private sector could help including:

◆ sponsor a school team; ◆ 'adopt' a facility; ◆ pay teachers' expenses for extra-curricular activities; ◆ sponsor coaches to work in schools; ◆ sponsor transport; ◆ sponsor sports equipment; ◆ sponsor inter-school competitions; ◆ sponsor links between schools and local sports clubs; ◆ sponsor sports scholarships for school pupils to a Centre of Excellence.

1 With your teacher's permission discuss what you think about the tobacco/alcohol sponsorship issue. Try to decide whether you would allow it to continue as it is, or bring in more controls.

2 Look at the Sports page of a daily newspaper, and find any mention of sponsorship. Bring what you've found to class, and with your teacher's permission share the information with your group.

3 Consider whether sponsorship makes you buy more of the sponsors' products.

23.4 Media

Local and national newspapers, magazines, radio and television, including satellite and cable TV, are all involved in reporting and broadcasting activities and events, and in interviewing the performers. They provide information for millions of people. The way in which this information is selected, and presented by producers, editors, reporters, and interviewers can influence the opinions of readers and audiences.

Satellite TV, with its 'pay as you watch' subscription channels, and ability to offer large amounts of money for exclusive broadcasting rights, is affecting the traditional pattern of media coverage in this country, and raises the question of whether Satellite TV should be allowed to dominate coverage of National Sporting Events. It may be that legislation may prevent subscription TV from 'owning' the broadcasting rights of important national events.

The audience that enjoys sport through the media is far larger than the number of people who take part, and the opportunities for sponsors to advertise their products are increasing.

At the Seoul Olympics *(1988)* the USA TV network, NBC, paid $300 million, Japanese TV paid $52 million, European broadcasters paid $28 million, and Eastern European broadcasters paid $3 million for the transmission rights. At the Winter Games of 1994 in Lillehammer, the USA TV network, CBS, paid $295 million; a large media centre was built 5 km from the town, and over 3000 reporters and photographers attended - easily out-numbering the 1000 or so competitors.

Organisers hope that the publicity will encourage more people to take part and spectate, so attracting more sponsorship. Sport has to look after the needs of the media if it is to prove attractive, especially to broadcasters and therefore sponsors. The media want to attract readers, listeners, and viewers; their coverage needs to be entertaining for their customers. The media can even become associated in people's minds with a particular event *(eg. the BBC and Wimbledon)*. The majority of events covered tend to be male and team dominated, although there are exceptions to this such as athletics. Women's events tend to get less coverage.

The BBC being publicly owned and paid for by licence fees, has a role in educating its audience as well as entertaining them. The profit motive is less important than it is with commercial stations. However, audience figures are increasingly important, as all stations try to capture as large a slice of the viewing/listening audience as possible.

The media now turn top performers into 'personalities' and 'stars'. They are used to comment on, and about, events, and appear on quiz and chat shows. The use of 'personalities' in this way can increase newspaper and magazine sales, radio audiences, and television viewing figures. This helps raise the profile of the newspaper or station, and for commercial bodies, attracts advertisers, increases sales and profits.

The way in which events are covered has also changed. Dramatic and tense moments make exciting viewing and news. There is now a greater coverage of such moments, by use of replays, special camera tricks, and close ups. The style of commentary has become much more informal, with a range of opinions being expressed. Opinions are now an essential element in most coverage.

Local media can make a positive contribution to school and club sport by becoming more involved in publicising and reporting events in their local area *('Raising the Game',1995)*. This increased local publicity can help to raise the profile of youth sport, and encourage more young people to become involved.

Action Box

1 Collect articles from newspapers, magazines, etc. which describe different events and competition. Ask your teacher if you can gather them together as a class.

2 Work out which activities are reported more than others.

3 Work out the balance of reporting between male and female activities.

4 The photo above is of an England v. New Zealand Women's Cricket World Cup. If this was the men's Test Match it would have had full coverage on the BBC. Do you think such coverage of the women's game would encourage more women to take up the sport?

23.5 Doping

The misuse of drugs in sport is not a new problem. As early as the 1904 Olympics *(St Louis, USA)* the marathon winner, Hicks *(USA)*, was suspected of taking drugs. The IOC developed systematic drug testing procedures in response to the apparent growth in the misuse of drugs in the 1960's. In the 1960 *(Rome)* Olympics, a Danish cyclist who had been using drugs, died of 'heat stroke', as did the British cyclist Tommy Simpson in the 1967 Tour de France. In 1966 the IOC formed its Medical Commission, and routine testing began in 1968 at the Grenoble Winter Games, and the Mexico Summer Games.

Issues concerning drug abuse continued throughout the years, but were highlighted at the 1988 Seoul games when weight lifters from India, Hungary, Romania and Britain all tested positive, along with a British judo fighter; and perhaps the most infamous of all, Ben Johnson *(Canada)*, after winning the 100 metres in a new world record, tested positive and had his medal taken away. The story of drug misuse in the Olympic Games parallels that in all sports, and in society as a whole.

Pressures

Many things may cause a performer to turn to drugs. The pressure to win may tempt individuals to use performance enhancing drugs. Therapeutic medications *(medicines used to increase the speed of healing)* are used to help performers get back into training quickly after an injury or illness. Social drugs also reduce the pressure of competition. Governing bodies try to prevent the misuse of drugs through coach and performer education, and testing *(although many performance improving drugs cannot yet (1997) be detected by testing)*.

Definition

The Sports Council has defined doping as:

"the taking or use of substances, or participation in doping methods, prohibited by the IOC and by International Sports Federations. In addition, assisting or inciting others to contravene doping regulations is also a doping offence."

Doping is a serious offence, and most governing bodies adhere to the IOC recommended list of doping classes, methods, and restricted drugs. The IOC list *(1993)* included the following.

◆ **Doping Classes (Types of Drugs)** - Stimulants, Narcotic Analgesics, Anabolic agents, Diuretics, Peptide Hormones and Analogues.

◆ **Doping Methods** - Blood doping; and Pharmacological, Chemical, and Physical Manipulation of the urine.

◆ **Classes of drugs subject to certain restrictions** - Alcohol, Marijuana, Local Anaesthetics, Corticosteroids, Beta-blockers.

The Sports Council's Doping Unit provides information on the banned classes of drugs. Let's look at some of these in more detail.

Tour de France.
Climbing the Col
d'Izoard towards
Briancon.

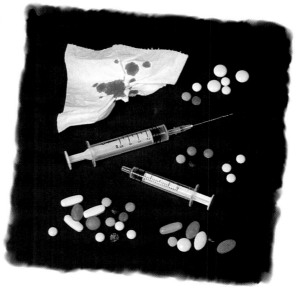

Doping Classes

Stimulants

These can be misused to delay tiredness and enhance aggression and competitiveness. However they can also cause an increase in body temperature, blood pressure and anxiety, an irregular and increased heart rate, a reduction in judgement, and loss of appetite.

Narcotic Analgesics

These are painkillers and are misused to deaden pain and allow the injured performer to keep going. They can cause breathing problems, vomiting, loss of concentration and coordination, and addiction. Carrying on performing whilst injured can make the injury worse, and could cause other injuries.

Anabolic Agents

These are are related to the male sexual hormone testosterone. Performers misuse them in order to improve power, strength and endurance, and so enhance performance. There are many physical and mental side-effects associated with their use, including aggression (*'roid rage'*), kidney and liver damage, and premature baldness. In women they cause the development of male features, for example deepening of the voice, facial hair, and coarser facial features. Growth hormone is also anabolic (*muscle building*), but as yet (*1996*) artificial use cannot be detected.

Diuretics

These aid water loss from the body (*see Making the weight: p.90*). Their misuse results in a rapid loss of weight. Side-effects include dehydration, muscle cramps, and interference with the functioning of the heart and kidneys as the volume of the blood and body fluids drops.

Peptide Hormones and Analogues

These stimulate the production of natural steroids and therefore the development of muscle.

It is important for performers to check with their governing bodies and seek advice on the exact types of substance that are banned. Ultimately, each individual is responsible for their use of any substance.

Doping Methods

Blood Doping - this is the giving of blood or related products to a competitor, other than for proper medical treatment. Blood may be taken from the competitor and freeze-stored. The person continues to train in this blood depleted state, until the body makes up the loss of blood. The blood that was taken out before, is then put back in, so that the competitor now has many more red blood cells than normal, which help carry more oxygen to the muscles. Although banned, blood doping cannot be detected.

The hormone EPO (*erythropoietin*) also increases the red blood cell count and is taken illegally by many endurance athletes.

Action Box

With the help and permission of your teacher. Set up two 'teams' amongst your friends, about 4 in a team will do:

1 One team must argue and justify the position that a performer should not be banned for life for misusing drugs to increase performance. Keep the argument focussed on the relationship between drugs and physical activity.

2 The other team must argue and justify the position that a performer should be banned for life for misusing drugs.

3 At the end of the debate the rest of the class must vote on the issue.

Testing

If a performer is selected for drug testing, there is a set procedure that is followed to ensure that each person is treated in the same way;

◆ the performer is notified of the testing;

◆ the person reports for testing with a representative from their activity;

◆ the performer selects a collection vessel, and provides a urine sample under the supervision of a testing officer;

◆ the performer selects a pair of pre-sealed bottle containers, breaks the security seals, and divides the sample approximately two thirds in one container and one third *(minimum 30 cm³)* in the other;

◆ the performer seals the bottles, and the testing officer records the bottle codes and seal numbers;

◆ the performer checks all this, signs to certify that everything is in order, and receives a copy of the form;

◆ the samples are then sent to an authorised lab, are tested, and a report is sent to the appropriate governing body;

◆ if the test is positive, performers are normally suspended, an analysis of the second sample can then be carried out, and a decision made about banning or not;

◆ the performer does have the right of appeal.

Testing can take place during training, and after competitions. They are carried out at random on those performers eligible for the relevant competitions. Random drug testing can also take place in National Schools Competitions. Testing tries to discourage those who might cheat, to identify performers who do cheat, and to protect those who do not. In the UK, testing is normally carried out by the Sports Council, although there may be other organisations involved in some cases.

Governing bodies need to be consistent in their approach to the problem. It is important that performers know what is banned, understand that testing will occur, and the consequences if they do not turn their backs on drug taking. The British Olympic Association has made it clear that any performer found guilty of the misuse of drugs will never be allowed to compete in the Olympic Games.

A high resolution Mass Spectrometer used for analysing urine samples.

The authorised doping control laboratory at King's

23.6 Hooliganism & Racist Behaviour

Hooliganism and racist behaviour is particularly associated with some sports rather than physical activities in general, for example Association Football has a history of such problems. This type of behaviour appears to have more to do with the problems in modern society than with football itself, and that a football match is simply the focus for violent and racist behaviour. It is also suggested that football has been, and is being, used by some people for political purposes. The same type of behaviour can be found in other countries such as Holland, Germany, and Italy.

The Taylor Report

Whatever the reasons, measures have been taken by the authorities to try and contain the problem. The Taylor Report, following the Hillsborough disaster, led to the introduction of all-seater stadiums *(which decrease bad spectator behaviour)*, and a greater emphasis on spectator safety. The police have developed sophisticated procedures, especially the use of video, for dealing with problems, before, during and after matches.

Football Related Arrests				
Total arrests per 100 000 spectators during a 5 year period, figures are the Police's combined league & cup match data.				
NCIS 1997 Press Release				
1992/93	1993/94	1994/95	1995/96	1996/97
25.8	21.5	19.9	16.8	16.7

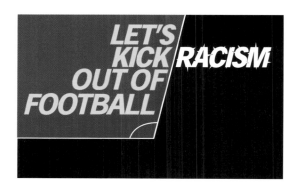

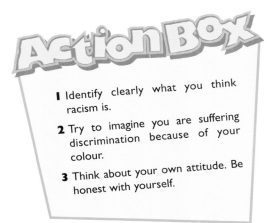

1 Identify clearly what you think racism is.

2 Try to imagine you are suffering discrimination because of your colour.

3 Think about your own attitude. Be honest with yourself.

Racist Abuse

Racist abuse has always existed, it is widespread, and is often focussed around sporting events, particularly professional football, where 25% of players are black.

In the 1970's extreme right wing political organisations began recruiting and selling their papers outside soccer grounds. At the same time black players increasingly became targets for racist abuse.

The problem continues, but many clubs work with fans to combat this type of behaviour. Racial discrimination can occur in other, less obvious ways; for example, at the beginning of 1998 only two managers of the 92 league clubs were black.

The 1991 Football *(Offences)* Act makes racist chanting illegal in England and Wales. This act was a consequence of the Taylor report, it created a separate offence of racist chanting. Anyone chanting insults based on colour, race, nationality, ethnic or national origins, can be prosecuted. Closed circuit TV is now used to identify individuals who behave in an offensive way.

In 1993 the Professional Footballers' Association *(the players union)* and the Commission for Racial Equality teamed up to campaign against racist abuse wherever it occurs in the sport, and bring equality of opportunity to all those who want to follow a career in professional football, under the banner 'Kick Racism Out of Football'.

This campaign is now sponsored by the Football Trust, Professional Footballers' Association, Football Association, and the Premier League. It is run by the organisation 'Kick It Out', in partnership with the Football League, League Managers' Association, Football Supporters' Association, Local Government Association, Football Safety Officers' Association, Metropolitan Police, GM Vauxhall Conference, and the Association of Premier and Football League Referees and Linesmen.

In 1994 a similar campaign began in Scotland. Racist problems also occur abroad, for example in Holland, Spain, Germany and Italy. In 1992 all the clubs in the two Italian leagues were involved in a 'No to Racism' campaign.

Surveys consistently show that these campaigns have the overwhelming support of the fans. Clubs tackle racist graffiti, make their opposition to racism clear, make public announcements on the issue before matches and during half time, ban the sale of racist literature around the grounds on match days, use cameras to identify offenders and adopt equal opportunities policies.

'Kick Racism Out of Football' is part of a wider movement aimed at the development of a just society where:

"everyone has an equal chance to work, learn, and live free from racial discrimination, and from the fear of racial violence, and harassment.' *(Commission for Racial Equality)*

23.7 Politics

Sport, and the arts, have long been used as political weapons to prove that one political system was better than another (*'Capitalism v Communism' and 'Fascism v Democracy' etc*), or one country's dominance over another (*Russia v USA etc*). They have also been linked to human rights issues; and linked to national policies (*South African Apartheid/ Russian invasion of Afghanistan etc*). These issues become interlinked with the prestige that international events bring to the host nation. The history of the Olympic Games reflects many of the political issues that have dominated the 20th century.

Politics and the Olympic Games

In Berlin *(1936)*, Hitler used the Olympic Games for propaganda purposes. He believed that the so-called 'aryan race' was superior to other 'races'. His secret police worked in the press corps. His racist views were upset when several black USA athletes, most notably Jessie Owens, won many events. Hitler refused to congratulate Owens even though he had congratulated German winners.

In Melbourne *(1956)*, Spain and Holland withdrew because the USSR had invaded Hungary. Taiwan (*an Island off China also known as Nationalist China*) was allowed to compete, so China withdrew; and Egypt and the Lebanon did not compete because of the Suez crisis, in which Britain and Israel invaded Egypt as a result of the dispute over the Suez canal.

In Tokyo *(1964)*, South Africa was not allowed to compete because of their apartheid (*segregating black, coloured and whites*) policy.

In Mexico City *(1968)*, many nations threatened to boycott the games if South Africa was allowed to compete. As a result the IOC withdrew the South African invitation. During the Games some black USA athletes wore black berets and raised clenched fists above their heads on the victory platform, in a black power salute, in protest at racial issues in the USA.

In Munich *(1972)*, 'Rhodesia' *(now Zimbabwe)* was not allowed to compete when most African nations threatened to withdraw as 'Rhodesia' had a white minority government. Palestinian terrorists killed 11 Israeli athletes after kidnapping them in the Olympic village. Five terrorists were killed and competitors from Syria, Egypt, and Kuwait left, frightened of retaliation. This tragedy sent shock waves around the world.

In Montreal *(1976)*, Taiwan was banned because the IOC only recognised China (*Mainland Communist China*), and black African nations withdrew because some New Zealand rugby players had toured South Africa.

In Moscow *(1980)*, many western nations, led by the USA, boycotted the Games because of the Soviet Union's invasion of Afghanistan in 1979. In fact the USSR had already been a controversial choice for the Games because of its Human Rights record. A West German delegate to the United Nations suggested that sporting links with the USSR should be cut. This illustrates the problems of the 'cold war' at this time. Only about half the expected competitors took part in the Games, but British athletes (*including Coe and Ovett*) competed, despite Government pressure not to do so.

Jessie Owens at the Berlin Olympics 1936. Starting blocks were not allowed, note the hole dug in the soft cinder track.

Jessie Owen's Gold Medal Performances	
100m Sprint	10.3s
200m Sprint	20.7s
Long Jump	8.06m
4x100m Relay	39.8s

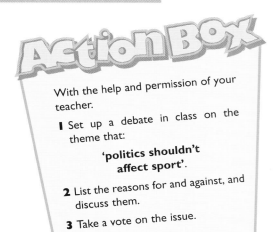

Action Box

With the help and permission of your teacher.

1 Set up a debate in class on the theme that:

'politics shouldn't affect sport'.

2 List the reasons for and against, and discuss them.

3 Take a vote on the issue.

In Los Angeles *(1984)*, the USSR, many Eastern European countries, and Cuba withdrew from the Games in retaliation for the 1980 Boycott of the Moscow Games. The official reason given expressed concern over the safety of their competitors.

The Olympics are not the only sporting events to provide examples of political interference. As the USA and China normalised relations, sport was used to develop the process, and the phrase 'ping-pong' diplomacy was born when table tennis tournaments were arranged for this purpose.

Apartheid

Apartheid was a major example of politics affecting sport. The Afrikaaner Nationalist Party won the 1948 election in South Africa, and introduced laws which discriminated against black South Africans. These included labour laws, the infamous pass laws *(movement restrictions and ID cards)*, segregated schooling, compulsory racial classification, and the 1950 'Group Areas' Act. The lifestyle of white South Africans improved considerably at the expense of the majority black population.

The international sporting community began to ban South Africa from international competitions because of the discrimination practised on entire racial groups. Some people argued that sport could be used as a way of pressuring South Africa into changing its policies. Gradually South Africa was isolated from the world sporting community. Anti-Apartheid groups in many countries campaigned against sporting contacts., and there were many problems in the 1960's, 1970's and 1980's. South Africa was expelled from the Olympic movement in 1970.

Following the Soweto riots in 1976, and the assassination of Steve Biko, a black South African organiser, in 1977 Commonwealth countries issued the Gleneagles Agreement, which discouraged sporting contacts with South Africa.

In the 1980's, the United Nations Special Committee against Apartheid began publishing lists of competitors who had visited and played in South Africa. However, in 1984, a young South African runner, Zola Budd, broke the women's World 5000 metres record, left South Africa and within two weeks became a British citizen. Demonstrations against her occurred.

In 1986, Britain refused to place economic sanctions on South Africa, and 32 countries boycotted the Commonwealth Games in protest. In 1989, the International Cricket Conference announced that cricketers who visited South Africa should be banned for life. Mike Gatting, a former England captain, led a rebel tour of South Africa. Demonstrations occurred inside and outside South Africa and the tour ended quickly.

South Africa was effectively a sporting outcast. The situation seemed deadlocked. Then, in 1990, President De Klerk began the slow process of getting rid of apartheid. The African National Congress was legalised and Nelson Mandela was released from prison. The national and international sporting bodies in South Africa became multi-racial, including the South African Olympic Committee. South Africa rejoined the Olympic movement in 1991. The process of reform continued, democratic elections were held, and Nelson Mandela was elected as President in 1994.

Nelson Mandela and the team captain of South Africa with the African Nations Cup *(soccer)* 1996.

Policies then focussed on integration and reconstruction, and South African sportsmen and women play a full part in international sport. The Rugby Union World Cup was held in South Africa in 1995 and the South African team won, they also won the first post-Apartheid Cricket Test Series against England which was held in South Africa in 1996. The African Nations Cup *(soccer)* was held in South Africa, and won by them, in 1996.

In the 1996 Centennial Olympic Games in Atlanta *(USA)* Hezekial Sepeng became the first black South African to win an Olympic medal when he came second in the 800 metres. The first black South African to win an Olympic gold medal was Josia Thugwane in the marathon a few days later.

Sporting isolation was one type of pressure used by the international community on South Africa. It is difficult to judge what effect it had over the years, in contributing to the change that has now occurred in South Africa. Nelson Mandela has stated his belief that the sporting boycott played an important part in the fight against apartheid. It did show the international communities condemnation of apartheid. The Olympic charter states that:

"...any form of discrimination...on the grounds of race.......
is incompatible with belonging to the Olympic movement."

Question Box ?

From what you have read, try to answer these questions.

1 What is the main difference between amateurs and professionals?

2 What type of activities do the media believe will attract larger audiences?

3 What do you think 'value for money' is for a sponsor?

4 What is doping?

5 What is racist chanting?

CHECK LIST

✔ Women have been traditionally associated with dance, & not other sports and adventurous activities.

✔ The main difference between amateurs and professionals is over methods of payment.

✔ Commercialisation is the process of organising events or performances along business lines.

✔ Sponsors want value-for-money.

✔ Private sector sponsors are encouraged to support local sports projects through the 'Sportsmatch Scheme'.

✔ The way the media reports events influences public opinion.

✔ Doping is concerned with the misuse of drugs.

✔ Hooliganism & racist chanting are associated with some sports rather than physical activities in general.

✔ Sport has been, and is, affected by politics.

✔ Apartheid is one example of the problematical relationship between sport & politics.

KEYWORDS

- Women's Sport Foundation
- Amateur
- Professional
- Commercialisation
- Sponsorship
- National Lottery
- Sportsmatch Scheme
- Media
- Doping
- Drug misuse
- Testing
- Hooliganism
- Racist Chanting
- Spectator
- Behaviour
- Politics
- Apartheid

Examination Box Three

1 Name one physical recreation activity in which you could take part.

(1 Mark)

2 Describe two reasons why you might take part in a physical recreation activity

(2 Marks)

3 List three personal factors that affect participation in physical recreation activities.

(3 Marks)

4 Identify three advantages of sponsorship for:

i) a sponsor;   *(3 Marks)*

ii) an activity.   *(3 Marks)*

5 The two tables below show the number of male members in five Association Football clubs between 1987 and 1989 *(Table 1)*, and the number of female members in five aerobics clubs between 1987 and 1989 *(Table 2)*

Table 1: Male members Association Football Clubs 1987–89

Club	1987	1988	1989
V	21	25	23
W	20	18	22
X	22	24	21
Y	23	28	25
Z	14	25	19

Table 2: Female members Aerobic Clubs 1987–89

Club	1987	1988	1989
A	16	18	17
B	20	22	20
C	14	17	16
D	15	19	16
E	15	24	21

i) What is the average female membership of the Aerobics clubs in 1987 *(Table 2)*?

(1 Mark)

ii) What is the percentage *(%)* increase in football club membership between 1987 and 1988 *(Table 1)*, and the percentage *(%)* decrease in Aerobic club membership between 1988 and 1989 *(Table 2)*?

(2 Marks)

iii) Briefly explain why relatively fewer women play football than take part in aerobics.

(5 Marks)

(Total Marks = 20)

Glossary

A

Acceleration
The rate of change of velocity over time *(where velocity is the rate of change of position with respect to direction).*

Adolescence
The stage of maturing into an adult, which involves more than sexual maturity.

Aerobic
Rhythmic, steady exercise which uses oxygen to oxidise glucose, fats, and proteins to release energy for the working muscles.

Agility
The ability to change the position of your body and/or its parts quickly and accurately.

Alactic Anaerobic Phosphagen system or process
The fastest source of energy in the body, using ATP and CP. Used in explosive strength, and speed activities.

Amateur
Participants who are not directly paid for performing. They take part for enjoyment and satisfaction, and not to make money.

Anabolic Steroids
Drugs based on the male hormone testosterone, which stimulate the building of more muscle tissue.

Anatomy
The internal structure of the body.

Antagonistic *(pairs of muscles)*
Most muscles in the body are arranged in opposing pairs. When one contracts, the other relaxes and is stretched, and vice versa. This arrangement is necessary as muscles can only contract (get shorter) when stimulated by motor nerves, they cannot restretch themselves.

Anxiety
Worry about what might happen in a situation. *(See also State Anxiety and Trait Anxiety).*

Assessment of physical activities
A process of judging/grading a person's level in relation to a set of criteria. In GCSE this involves a process of planning, performing, evaluating, analysing, and improving chosen physical activities.

Associative Stage of learning
The second stage of learning. Patterns of coordination are learnt, motor programmes begin to be laid down in the brain.

ATP *(Adenosine Triphosphate)*
The substance through which all energy to be used in the body is channelled . Once used to supply energy to some process, eg. muscle contraction, it must be reformed using energy from other sources, eg. the oxidation of glucose.

$$ATP \rightarrow ADP + P + energy$$
to be used
by the body

$$ADP + P + energy \rightarrow ATP$$
from the
oxidation
of glucose

Autonomous Stage of learning
The third stage of learning. The movement has been learned, and the performer has time to think about tactics, strategies, style, expression, and the fine tuning of skills.

B

Balance
Maintaining the equilibrium of the body, either without movement *(static balance)* or during movement *(dynamic balance).*

Base of Support
The base of support involves the relationship between you and the surface you are performing on.
It includes the points of contact you have with the surface you are performing on.

Body Composition
The relative proportions of fat and lean *(non-fat)* body mass.

C

Carbohydrates
Energy rich substances, eg. starch, found in foods like bread, potatoes, pasta, etc. Starch is digested to glucose which is absorbed by the body.

Cardiac Output
The amount of blood pumped out by the heart per minute.

Cardiac Output	=	Stroke Volume	x	Heart Rate

Centre of Gravity *(of the body)*
The point about which your body weight is evenly distributed in any position.

Circuit Training
Training that uses a circuit of exercises around a number of different work stations. Each circuit lasting about 20 minutes.

Closed Skills
These are performed in predictable and stable conditions. The performer tries to repeat the movement the same way each time, eg. a free shot in basketball.

Cognitive Stage of learning
The first stage of learning. Beginners learn to understand what they have to do.

Commercialisation
The process of organising an event or performance along business lines.

Community Physical Recreation
An attempt to provide individuals, and groups with access and opportunities in a range of physical recreational activities, at a local neighbourhood level. The idea of 'community' brings a more 'human' feeling to such provision.

Compulsory Competitive Tendering - CCT
Forcing Local Authority leisure centres etc. to allow various groups to bid for contracts to supply various services.

Concentric *(muscle action)*
Muscles shorten as they contract. When they shorten normally, eg. in a biceps curl, it is also known as an isotonic contraction. When stopped from shortening very much by an immovable resistance, it is also known as an isometric contraction.

Coordination
The ability to control, and put together *(integrate)* movements made by different parts of the body.

Cramp
A sudden, uncontrollable, painful contraction of a muscle or a group of muscles, that may last for only seconds, or for hours at a lower intensity. Of unknown cause, but loss of salts can be a cause. Treated by stretching and massage.

Creatine Phosphate *(CP)*
An energy reserve in the muscles that is used to regenerate ATP after it has been used in muscle contractions.

$$ADP + CP \rightarrow ATP + C$$

Decision Making
This involves you in making a decision about what action to perform, after you have been through the process of giving meaning to information, and comparing the information received with your memories.

Discrimination
This is the act of distinguishing between people on the grounds of sex, race, religion. etc. and dealing differently with them because of these perceived differences.

Distributed Practice
Practise of an activity with rest breaks in the practice session.

Doping
The taking or mis-use of substances, or participation in doping methods, prohibited by the IOC and by the International Sports Federations. In addition, assisting or inciting others to contravene doping regulations is also a doping offence.

Dual Use
The sharing of school and other educational facilities with users who are not pupils, students, or staff.

Eccentric *(muscle action)*
When a muscle is trying to contract whilst actually being lengthened by stretching, eg. the thigh muscles while running down hill.

Endocrine Glands
Glands without ducts *(tubes)* which produce hormones, and pass them direct into the bloodstream, eg. pituitary, thyroid, and adrenal glands.

Endurance
Stamina, the ability to keep going for long periods. Includes cardiovascular-respiratory *(heart-breathing)* endurance, and muscular endurance.

Enzymes
Chemicals *(proteins)* produced by living organisms, which act as catalysts, ie. they speed up the rate of chemical reactions in the body, without themselves being used up in the reaction.

Excellence
Achieving standards above average, nationally set performance targets encourage performers to strive for excellence.

Excretion
Getting rid of poisonous waste products produced by the body, eg. carbon dioxide *(by breathing out)*, and urea in the urine from the kidneys.

Exercise
Involves exertion of the body. It is important in maintaining general health, and includes cardiovascular-respiratory *(heart-breathing)* endurance, muscular endurance, strength, mobility and flexibility, and body composition. *(See also Physical fitness)*.

Extrinsic Feedback
This is information given to the performer from an outside source, eg. teacher/ coach/ video/ spectator etc. It can be in the form of Knowledge of Results, and/or Knowledge of Performance. These are always external in origin. It is also called Supplementary Feedback and Augmented Feedback.

Extroversion
A personality factor (trait) which involves sociability, talkativeness, and self assurance.

Fartlek
'Speed play', running as you please, fast and slow, over different terrains.

Fats
Energy rich substances, eg. butter, oils, etc.

Feedback
Information you receive about your actions, in the form of Knowledge of Results and Knowledge of Performance. *(See also Extrinsic Feedback and Intrinsic Feedback)*.

Fine Motor Skills
Involve movements using small groups of muscles in delicate actions, eg. wrist action in table tennis.

First Aid
This is the treatment given by the first person to arrive on the scene of an accident. It is better if the first aider is properly trained.

Flexibility
The range of movement at a joint allowed by the muscles *(length & elasticity)* that surround it.

Force
Force can be described as a 'pull' or a 'push'.

Gender
Which sex a person is, eg. male or female.

Goal setting
Process of setting performance targets or goals, and organising ways of achieving these goals. Goals should be Specific, Measurable, Agreed, Realistic, Time phased, Exciting, and Recorded - SMARTER.

Goals
Standards of performance to be aimed for. Can be based on your own performance, eg. achieving a personal best - Performance Based Goals; or on your performance compared to others, eg. position in a race - Outcome Goals.

Gross Motor Skills
These are skills which involve large groups of muscles, eg. discus throwers.

Health
A state of complete physical, mental, and social well-being, and not only the absence of disease or infirmity.

Hooliganism
Anti-social, threatening, and rowdy behaviour

Hormone
A chemical 'messenger' produced by an endocrine gland. Very small amounts have powerful effects on the body, eg. adrenaline 'pumps the body up' for activity.

Information Processing
A model of the way in which a skill is learnt. It tries to explain what goes on when you turn information you receive into movements.

Isometric Muscle Action
Occurs when a muscle starts to contract and shorten, but is then stopped by an immovable resistance, eg. trying to lift a weight that is too heavy for you to move.

Isotonic Muscle Action
Normal muscle action, when the muscle shortens as it produces movement, eg. a biceps curl.

Interference with learning
When established skills which have already been learnt, interfere with the learning of new skills, and new skills interfere with existing skills. For example a tennis player might find it difficult to learn badminton, and that in trying to learn it, their tennis gets worse.

Interval Training
Training with alternating work intervals and rest intervals, eg. 6 x 200m with 60 seconds rest between each 200m run.

Intrinsic Feedback
This is information you give to yourself from your actions or from the activity. It can be in the form of Knowledge of Results *(you see/hear it)*, and/or Knowledge of Performance *(you feel it)*.

Introversion
A personality dimension, where the person is withdrawn, anxious, and insecure.

Inverted U Theory
Motivation *(arousal)* increases to an optimum point, at which performance is at its best, past which control and quality of performance decreases through trying too hard and becoming anxious.

Involuntary Muscle
Muscle that you cannot control by your conscious decisions.

Joint Provision
The providing of new facilities for the shared use of different groups, eg. school, and public.

Joule
A measure of energy. 4.2 joules = 1 calorie.

Knowledge of Performance *(KP)*
Is a type of feedback in which a performer receives information about the quality of their performance in terms of movement, style, etc. When given by a coach/video it is extrinsic. When felt by the performer it is intrinsic.

Knowledge of Results *(KR)*
Is a type of feedback in which a performer receives information about the results of their actions. When given by a coach/video it is extrinsic. When seen/heard directly by the performer it is intrinsic.

Lactic Acid
An acid produced by muscles working powerfully without enough oxygen *(anaerobically)*. The increased acidity stimulates faster breathing, and causes muscle pain.

Lactic Anaerobic System
The way in which energy is released from glycogen *(glucose)* without using oxygen *(anaerobic)*, and which results in the production of lactic acid in the muscles.

Learning Curve
A graphical depiction of the progress of learning *(or lack of it)*.

Leisure
That time not spent working, eating, and sleeping, which is available for your own recreation.

Levers
A structure with a pivot point about which an effort moves a load. There are three types of lever according to the different positions of the effort, load, and pivot.

Limited Channel Capacity
The information processing model that emphasises that the brain can only deal with a limited amount of information at once. You could become confused and overloaded by too much information.

Local Provision
Local facilities for sport, provided by public, private, and voluntary organisations.

Long Term Memory
A more permanent memory store. When information is practised and coded, it passes from the short term memory into the long term memory, from where it can be retrieved *(recalled)* using the coded memory keys.

Manual/Mechanical Guidance
Physical help in learning what to do.

Massed Practice
Practise of an activity without any rest breaks in the practice session.

Mechanical disadvantage
When the arrangement of the pivot, effort, and load, of a lever system results in the effort having to be greater than the load.

Media
A term used to describe local and national newspapers, magazines, radio, and television, which are all involved in reporting and broadcasting activities and events, and in interviewing the performers.

Memory
A storage and retrieval *(finding)* system.

Mental Practice
Imagining the successful performance of an activity.

Metabolic Rate
The rate at which your body uses energy. This rate can vary depending on level of activity, health and fitness.

Motion
Movement and the change of position, including the idea of speed.

Motivation
Reflects the commitment and determination of a performer. It is a general level of arousal *(intensity)* to action. It involves a sense of purpose, direction, and sustainment. Intrinsic motivation is when the source of motivation comes from the individual *(enjoyment, satisfaction)*, and extrinsic motivation is when the source of motivation comes from a source other than yourself *(prizes, money, etc.)*.

Motor Programmes
Patterns of muscle commands recorded in the central nervous system which can be used quickly when needed.

Motor *(movement)* **Skill**
There isn't a single, agreed definition of a motor skill. We could say that motor skill is, "the learned ability to perform in a physical activity efficiently, successfully, and consistently".

Movement Time
The time it takes to actually move as a result of the brain sending nerve impulses to the muscles. Part of the response time.

National Curriculum
Programmes of study and attainment targets laid down by the Government, stating what pupils must study from the time they enter primary school, to when they take GCSE in year 11. It is divided into 4 Key Stages, and Maths, English, Science are the core subjects.

Neuroticism
A personality factor *(trait)* which involves sensitivity, anxiety and insecurity.

Newton's Third Law
To every action there is an equal and opposite reaction.

Olympic Ideal
The Olympic Ideal is expressed in the idea of Olympism, which is an outlook on life which includes the enjoyment of taking part, trying hard, fair play, respect for the rules, and the pursuit of excellence. The Olympic movement exists to promote these ideals.

Open Skill
These are performed in situations which are continually changing so that the performer has to adapt the skill to the changing situation, eg. tackling in football.

Overload of training *(see Progressive Loading)*

Overloading of information
Receiving too much information at once, causing confusion. A part of information Processing Theory.

Oxygen Debt
The amount of oxygen taken up after intense exercise has stopped. It is needed to oxidise the lactic acid that was produced by the release of energy from glucose without oxygen *(anaerobically)* during the intense activity. See also Oxygen deficit.

Oxygen Deficit
The amount of oxygen a performer is short of during intense exercise in which they are getting energy from glucose without oxygen *(anaerobically)*. (See also Oxygen debt).

P.E. *(See Physical Education)*.

Parts Learning
Breaking a skill down to its basic parts, which are then learnt one at a time, before putting them altogether in the complete skill. If you join each part together as they are learned, it is called progressive parts *(stages)*.

Participation
The taking part in physical activities.

Perception
To understand *(give meaning to)* what has been seen, heard, and felt. The first step in interpreting information. Acts as a filter, and helps you separate out important information from the less important.

Personality
A person's character and temperament. A complex series of factors, unique to the individual.

Phosphagen System
See 'Alactic anaerobic phosphagen system'.

Physical Education - P.E.
A foundation subject in the National Curriculum. It involves people in learning and taking part in physical activities. It could help develop a more positive attitude towards yourself, and to life. It is, for many people, the same as playing games, taking part in many different physical activities, or keeping fit. It is through these types of activities at school that learning happens, and Physical Education is taught. Physical Education focuses on bodily movement, and involves the development of enjoyment, understanding, co-ordination, and control. The overall aims are to develop:
◆ physical skills and abilities;
◆ knowledge and understanding;
◆ positive attitudes to activity and health;
◆ social awareness.

Physical Fitness
The capacity to perform physical activity with relative success and enjoyment without undue discomfort during or after. This normally involves a measure of the relative efficiency of the heart, blood vessels, lungs and muscles, in carrying out movements. In hard physical activity the enjoyment involves knowing that you have achieved your aims.

Physical Recreation
This is entertaining oneself, or relaxing, in leisure time, through physical activity.

Physiology
The study of how the body works.

Physique
The physical build of the body.

Planning *(of training)*
The organising of a training programme. Account should be taken of frequency, intensity, time *(duration)*, and type of exercise - F.I.T.T.

Plateau
A period in learning when no progress appears to be made.

Politics
Politics involves the principles, ideas, and government concerned with the practical and theoretical aspects of social organisation.

Posture
The way all the parts of the body are aligned together.

Power
The rate at which work is done:

$$\text{Power} = \frac{\text{work}}{\text{time}} = \frac{\text{force} \times \text{distance}}{\text{time}}$$

Professional
Participants who are paid for performing. They earn their living from the activity.

Progressive Loading *(Overload of training)*
Increasing the training effort in carefully controlled stages - not actually overloading in the sense of overstraining the body and its systems, which could lead to injury.

Proteins
Substances which build and repair the body, especially muscle. Protein containing foods must be eaten every day, eg. meat, eggs, cheese, nuts, soya beans etc.

Puberty
The beginning of the development of sexual maturity.

Pulse
The rhythmic beat of the blood being pumped by the heart through the arteries, which are swollen in diameter when the heart contracts, and recoil back to normal when the heart relaxes. Can be felt at the wrist and at the side of the neck.

R

Racist Behaviour
This is behaviour that develops from the idea of the superiority of one race *(a division of humankind whose members share certain characteristics)* over another. This usually involves behaviour that is abusive, often violent, and discriminatory.

Reaction Time
The time it takes for the brain to receive information, to decide what to do, and to send impulses to the muscles. Part of the response time.

Recovery Position
The position to place an injured person into if possible, and if safe to do so.

Relaxation
A process of reducing tension, rigidity, anxiety, and intensity. Specific techniques can be developed, eg. Progressive Muscular Relaxation, the Quiet Place, Centring.

Response Time
The time it takes to respond to some stimulus, eg. the actions of people.

$$\underset{\text{Time}}{\text{Response}} = \underset{\text{Time}}{\text{Reaction}} + \underset{\text{Time}}{\text{Movement}}$$

Where the reaction time is the time it takes the brain to receive information, to decide what to do, and to send impulses to the muscles; and the movement time is the time it takes to actually move.

Reversibility *(of training)*
Gains in fitness as result of training are not permanent, they are easily lost *(reversed)* if training stops.

Rules
The laws/regulations governing participation in a physical activity.

S

Safe
Being free from danger or harm. What you must always be!

Selective Attention
A process of focussing your mind (attention) on important information *(actions, stimuli, etc.)*. A part of Information Processing theory.

Sensory Input
Information received from the senses, eg. sight, sound, touch, taste, smell, and feelings.

Short Term Memory
A temporary memory store, from which information is easily forgotten. Information that is considered significant is coded and practised, and passed on into Long Term Memory.

Somatotyping
The classification of body types *(physique)* on the basis of basic skeletal structure, into endomorph, mesomorph, and ectomorph.

Specificity *(of training)*
Different types of training improve different *(specific)* parts and systems of the body, eg. cycling will not help a swimmer improve their swimming.

Speed
The distance covered in a certain time.

Sponsorship
The giving of money or other material goods to an activity, event, organisation, performance, or individual(s), by a sponsor, in return for which, the goods/services of the sponsor are publicised/advertised.

Sport
This term is used in many different ways. It could be described as "a type of physical activity which you choose to compete in fairly, and try to win." There have been many attempts to divide sport into different groups.

Stability *(of personality)*
A personality dimension involving calmness and a feeling of security.

Stability *(of the body)*
This involves the equilibrium or balance of the body on a base, it is increased if:
the area of the base is wider or larger;
the centre of gravity is lowered;
the centre of gravity is brought nearer to the centre of the base.

State Anxiety
Anxiety which is caused by/related to a specific situation, eg. a rock face.

Stitch
A pain in the chest/abdomen region associated with running. Of unknown cause, but possibly a result of the jarring action of running acting on the liver, which is suspended below the diaphragm on the right hand side.

Strength
The amount of force that is produced by muscles contracting.
Includes static or isometric strength, where effort is made against an immovable resistance; and dynamic or isotonic strength where effort moves a resistance.

Stretching
Exercise to improve flexibility. This can be passive, eg. limb being pushed to the limit of movement by a partner; active, eg. moving and holding your own stretch position; and ballistic, eg. swinging arms and/or legs.

Stroke Volume
The volume of blood pumped out by each contraction of the ventricles of the heart.

Supplementary Feedback
(See Extrinsic Feedback).

Techniques
The basic patterns of movement which have to be developed in every activity.

Trace Decay *(forgetting)*
The fading away of a memory which has been learned but not practised or used.

Training *(physical)*
A process which is designed to improve physical capacity, fitness, skill, etc.

Transfer of Training *(learning)*
The influence of previously learned skills and activities on the learning of new ones. This appears to depend on the amount of similarity between the skills and activities, and may be helpful *(positive)* or harmful *(negative)*.

Trait Anxiety
A personality factor *(trait)*. The tendency to become anxious in almost all or any situation.

Variation *(of training)*
Training should be varied to prevent boredom occurring and injuries developing. Variation should always be safe.

Vascularisation
The growth of new capillary networks in muscles working aerobically over long periods of time. It increases their potential blood supply, and therefore their oxygen supply during aerobic exercise. Similar changes as a result of aerobic training occur within the coronary arteries of the heart muscle.

Verbal Guidance
Telling a performer what to do to improve their performance.

Visual Guidance
Showing a performer how to improve their performance.

Voluntary Muscle
Muscle that can be controlled by your conscious decisions.

Warm-down *(cool down)*
A warm-down brings the mind and the body back to a relaxed state. Helps to reduce the risk of injury.

Warm-up
A warm-up should involve a gradual increase in the heart rate and breathing rate, a slight rise in body temperature, and prepare the mind and the body for activity. Helps to reduce the risk of injury.

Whole Learning
Learning a skill as a complete action, without breaking it down into its basic parts. Faulty parts can then be identified and attempts made to improve them. If the faulty part is isolated and practised, and the skill then performed as a whole again, this is called whole-part-whole learning.

Index

Page numbers in bold indicate a main heading in the text.

Page numbers in bold indicate a main heading in the text.

Page numbers in bold indicate a main heading in the text.

S-Z